The Quest for Immortality

Kamil V Zvelebil

Mandrake of Oxford

First edition

Mandrake of Oxford

PO Box 250

Oxford, OX1 1AP

Britain

British Library CIP Data
Zvelebil, Kamil V.
Siddha Quest for Immortality
I. Title
294.523
ISBN 1 869928 43-1

Printed in Great Britain by
Antony Rowe Ltd, Chippenham, Wiltshire

Contents

Note: The Tamil and Sanskrit (and occasional Hindi etc.) terms and names are given in broad (mostly Anglicized) transcription without diacritical marks. An index of these terms and names in precise transliteration is appended to this book.

Preface

Whereas in a previous publication of 1973 (reprint 1993) I dealt almost exclusively with Tamil[1] Siddha poetry,[2] the present book will be concerned with Tamil Siddhas as poets and with their writings as part of Tamil literature only marginally.

The Siddhas are not a particular Tamil phenomenon. They are not an isolated, unique body of freethinkers, but an integral part of a pan-Indian movement and tradition;[3] at least one of them was apparently a Muslim .

According to Mircea Eliade,[4] the Siddhas are, in India, those rather original thinkers "who understood liberation as the conquest of immortality". Specifically, however, South Indian, Tamil Siddhism manifests the following features: the quest of perfect health and 'immortality' or at least longevity in this present life, and hence prevailing preoccupation with medicine and alchemy; development of occult powers, so-called siddhis; the application of basic techniques of Hatha Yoga; a religious component of anti-ritualism and suppression of devotion in favour of the search for knowledge and personal experience; a philosophical component of deep relativism and pessimism; loathing and abhorrence of women which, however, quite often and paradoxically combines with Tantrik-like use of sexual congress; a very important social component expressed as social radicalism and attacks on the Hindu 'establishment'; and the use of strong, even obscene, but dark and ambiguous language.

This book deals mostly but not exclusively with the Siddha preoccupation with medicine, healing and therapies, with sexual attitudes and yoga, as preserved and expressed in ancient texts composed in Tamil as well as in the living practices of contemporary Siddha physicians. It is necessary to stress that the Siddha tradition lives on in Tamilnadu,

---

1 Tamil is a Dravidian language of South India, spoken by about 60 million (Lane 1984) in the State of Tamilnadu (formerly roughly Madras State), in Sri Lanka, and by Tamil settlers in Burma, Vietnam, Malaysia, Indonesia, East and South Africa, Singapore, Mauritius and elsewhere. The earliest literary monuments of Tamil belong to c. 3rd cent. B.C.. For Dravidian and Tamil in general, cf. my *Dravidian Linguistics - an Introduction*, Pondicherry Institute of Linguistics and Culture, 1990.

2 *The Poets of the Powers*, Rider, London, 1973. Reprint, Integral Publishing, Lower Lake, California, 1993.

3 See for details chapter 3 of my 1973 (1993) publication.

4 Eliade, Mircea, *Yoga, Immortality and Freedom*, Princeton, 1969, p.304.

although it may not be always very easy to find its genuine expressions. However, the poetry and writings, that is, literary writings of early medieval and medieval Siddhas will also be dealt with, but not as the chief concern of this work.

My thanks are first and foremost due to all my Siddha informants, in particular to the physician who belonged to the lineage of Yakkopu and spent his life between the town of Palani, the sacred site of the cult of god Murugan - Dandapani[5] and Madras, where he had a medical practice. I am also grateful , for their assistance and suggestions, to my former Tamil teacher Mahavidvan M. V. Venugopala Pillai (1896 - 1985), to my friend and adviser, the scholar Mayilai Sini. Venkataswamy (1900 - 1980), and to my closest Tamil friend Mr. R. Kannan of Madras. A few more specifically biomedical aspects were discussed with my daughter Dr. M. J. J. Zvelebil and with Prof. Dr. J. Vincent, both of them experts in their respective fields, quite removed from my own. I must not forget to mention the patience and understanding of Kris Morgan, my Mandrake publisher.

Kamil V. Zvelebil
Cabrespine, France

---

5 Murugan (alias Velan, The Spear-Bearer, and Ceyyon, The Red One, worshipped at Palani as Dandapani, the ascetic club-bearer) is most probably a pre-Aryan, Dravidian god of youth and beauty, virility and victorious war and, at the same time, a sort of 'national' Tamil deity. He is of special significance to the Siddhas, as is his Sakti Pongi - Valli - Valai. For details, see p. 130 of my 1973 (1993) book, and also my *Tamil Traditions on Subrahmanya-Murugan*, Institute of Asian Studies, Madras, 1991, as well as 'Mythologie der Tamilen und anderer drawidisch sprechender Völker', von K. V. Zvelebil, in: H. W. Haussig, *Wörterbuch der Mythologie*, Klett-Cotta Verlag, Stuttgart, 1974, 907-13.

Cunnilingus according to Tantrik Siddhas
[from a late medieval text in Tamil entitled Kâmapânacâstiram *Treatise on the Arrow of Lust*]

First Stage
Like a cow which licks tenderly its calf
spread out your tongue broad
and lick her yoni [6]
lapping up the juices oozing out
like a thirsty dog which laps cool water

Second stage
Like a worshipper who circumambulates the shrine
pass your tongue over her yoni
round around from left to right,
moving in ever narrowing circles
till you reach the very centre.
Her yoni will open up
like a dark and gaping chasm.
Open then the vulva's lips
with firm pressure of your tongue
and insert its stiff tip inside
like a spear's powerful thrust,
digging, poking deep and far.

Third stage
With you nose pressing against the yonimani [7]
your tongue enters her innermost shrine
thrusting and digging and poking deep,
searching for hidden treasures inside.
Inhale deeply, breathing in the mellow odours
of the juices of her yoni.

---

6 *yoni* = vagina, vulva; the entire female generative organ
7 *yonimani*, lit. vulva-jewel = clitoris

Fourth stage

Take the protruding, throbbing jewel of her yoni
gently, gently between your teeth and tongue,
suck it like a suckling feeding at the breast;
it will rise and glisten, stand up from its sheath.
It will swell like a large ruby.
The fragrant copious discharge
appearing like sweet foam
between the lips of the vulva
is a rejuvenating drink
when mixed with your milk-white,
lustrous, thick and fragrant sperm

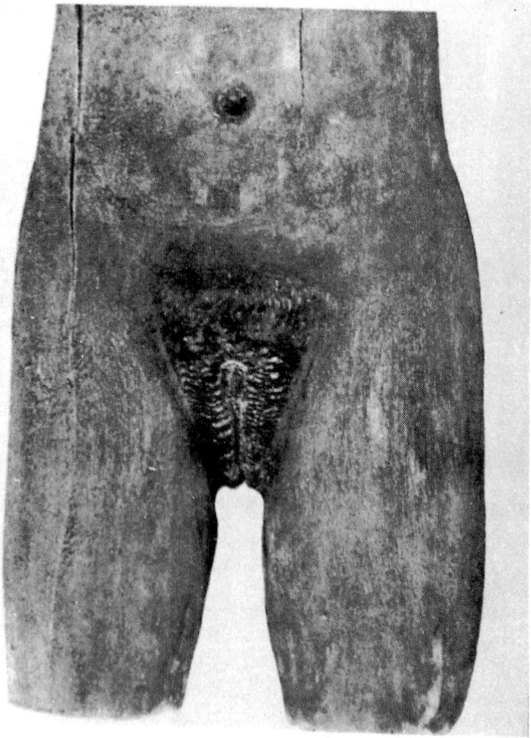

1. Picture of Yoni (female genitals) used in initiatory rites of tantriks and worshippers of Shakti. Shaktism and Tantrism are one of the ideological bases of Siddha doctrines. South Indian Woodcut, contemporary.

2
Foreword

The Tamil Siddhas cannot be regarded as one homogenous 'movement' or 'school of thought' manifesting a unified, well-defined, uniform ideology. A great number of elements have entered into their thinking, some of them pan-Indian, some of them apparently specifically South Indian or Tamil. On the other hand, their overall ideology has, of course, several basic doctrinal tenets in common. As we shall see, some of these tenets are in amazing correspondence with the most recent developments in modern physics of post-relativity and quantum theory era. The schema of dense and subtle matter is one of those tenets: according to ultimate Siddha thought, subtle matter constitutes the inner body of man; matter is nothing but crystallized energy, and a manifestation of infinite and universal mind[1] ('subtle matter' reappears in the theories of physicists of our day). An accomplished Siddha is someone who has learned to harmonize his awareness with this subtle (sub-atomic?) matter of which he is composed. The Siddha alchemist can live in the mode of constant appearance and disappearance, manifestation

---

1 This, of course, is not *specifically* Siddha tenet. It is an ancient Indian postulate which appears in Hindu models as well as in some, notably Mahayana, Buddhist thought. The Upanishads speak of pure consciousness residing in every being like 'butter hidden in cream', the whole universe being but 'materialized' Brahman. Some schools of Mahayana Buddhism speak of 'mind only' (*cittamatra*; Vijnanavada school of Mahayana Buddhism postulates an undifferentiated consciousness).

and dissolution, of subtle matter and energy; and all matter forms a continuum. Neither matter nor consciousness are ultimate, for both have their source in something still 'beyond', in Civam which can not really become object of knowledge. Hence the Siddha poet speaks often of 'silence'[2]:

Silence, unmoved and rising,
Silence, unmoved and sheltering,
Silence, unmoved and permanent,
Silence, unmoved and brilliant,
Silence, broad and immense like the Ganga,
Silence, unmoved and increasing,
Silence, white and shining like the Moon,
Silence, the Essence of Siva.[3]

The only possible predication of the 'something' in which both matter and consciousness have their source is Void, Emptiness. Hence, again, one of the key-terms appearing in Siddha poetry: *vettaveli, cuniyam* 'utter emptiness, void', *veliyirveli* (liter.) 'void in emptiness' i.e. supreme, absolute Emptiness; or, simply, *veli* (liter 'open space; space; openness') 'emptiness':[4]

---

2 Cf. the universal fact that, *ultimately*, all that remains is only silence. Johannes Meister Eckhart (c. 1260 - c. 1327) knew it; Wittgenstein's (1889 - 1951) dictum on this topic is famous. Christian theology itself, in its true depths, arrives at analogous conclusions: Christ is regarded as God's Word proceeding from *silence* (Ignatius of Antioch). Paul (Rom. 16. 25) speaks of 'the mystery that had remained *silent* for eternal ages'. Mary is 'mute mother of the *silent* Word' (De Lubac, *Meditations sur l'eglise*, Paris, 1983, p. 260); Pascal speaks of *silence* in love which 'is worth more than discourse', etc. And, from Indian tradition, cf. the Buddha's dictum (*Prasannapada*, LVII, 8) 'The most noble of the truths is *silence*'. The Buddha maintained 'noble silence' when it came to matters which are *avyakrtavastuni*, that is, which cannot be answered by means of any logical predication.

3 K. V. Zvelebil, *The Poets of the Powers*, Integral Publishing, 1993, p. 86: Civavakkiyar's poem No. 332.

4 The terms *veli* etc. are of Dravidian origin (cf. *Dravidian Etymological Dictionary* entry 5498) whereas the analogical term *cuniyam* is derived from Sanskrit *sunya-*.

Gods made out of wood
    Gods made out of stone
Gods made out of palmyra fronds
    Gods made out of bone
Gods made out of rags
    Gods made out of dung
Gods made out of saffron bags
    There are no other gods
        but
        VOID
    (Civavakkiyam 503 / 510)[5]

It must be stressed, however, that by this emptiness is not meant a substantive emptiness like 'an empty box'. It is emptiness which is a plenum (more about all this will be said in subsequent chapters). And man can come into contact with this Void. How, that is precisely what the Siddhas tell us.

These, then, are, in very simplified words, some of the ultimate and basic doctrinal points common to all those thinkers, poets, alchemists and physicians designated as cittar (Siddhar, Siddhas) in Tamil India. Now, to speak of less lofty matters, the reader must be made aware that, nowadays, when it comes to Siddha medicine and medical practice, there even exist, in Madras, a government Siddha dispensary, and a government Siddha medical college. Also, let us return to what divides the Siddhas from one another; let us mention at least one of their important 'inhomogeneities' - the Siddha attitude to sex.

The Siddha attitude to sex often manifests features which are in mutual contrast, and thus represents a good illustration of the heterogeneous character of the Siddha 'movement'. On the one hand there are Siddha poets who express utter disgust and revulsion towards women and any sexual activity (e. g. Pattinattar who in Potu 14 speaks of men who 'for the sake of a cunt / perish day and night', and in 31 mentions ' women / who smell of their / sensuality', whose 'limbs stink of their discharge'). Pattinattar is not the only one, although he probably represents the most vigorous manifestation of the ascetic, stern,

---

5 The difference in numbering reflects different editions of the texts. For Civavakkiyar and his poetry see the brief reader of Siddha texts at the end of the book.

misogynist trend of Siddha thought. On the other hand, in drastic contrast - so at least it seems - there is an entire group of Siddha alchemist-medicine men who are obviously raised in the Tantrik tradition, and who in fact take part in rituals based on the Tantrik *cakrapuja*. This stream of Siddha thought and practice will be dealt with in some detail in chapter 12 of this book, but here I wish to indicate very briefly the most salient features of such Tantrik-Siddha ritual.

In the centre of a ritual circle (*cakkiram*) sits a chosen woman, completely naked, who symbolizes Devi, i. e. Sakti, the Primeval Energy of the Cosmos, the Goddess, and it is characteristic of the Siddha views that caste or community is of absolutely no importance either in the selection of this woman (she can be a virgin as well as a prostitute, a young Brahmin girl as well as a ripe low-caste lady), or in the gathering of the participants. This Sakti, thoroughly washed and perfumed all over her body with various perfumes (according to an exact prescription; for details cf. chapter 12), sits on a sort of pedestal with widely spread legs so that her *yoni* (vulva) is well visible. The leading Siddha will kiss the *yoni*, and bless various non-vegetarian foodstuffs through the contact with the *yoni* by touching and rubbing with them the vulva of the Sakti. Then these offerings are distributed among the participants and consumed. The participating men, who for five days preceding the *puja* had been eating meat, drinking alcoholic beverages and using aphrodisiacs according to Siddha pharmacopoeia, will naturally be in a state of high sexual arousal which must however be strictly controlled, until ritual cohabitation follows with their chosen female partners which - and this is a basic and most important requirement - must never end in ejaculation of the sperm. The Siddha tenet underlying all this holds that the enormous force which is released by controlled sexual tension must be translated from the gross physical level to the 'subtle' body and ultimately to the psychic level whereby one attains various *siddhis* or supranormal powers and 'immortality'.

This book consists of some sixteen sections. The introductory chapter describes in broad outlines general features of Siddha medicine (since this is what the book is mostly concerned with), and in the following chapter are spelled out ideological tenets of the specific Siddha quest of immortality. Next chapter deals with basic principles and beliefs of Siddha physicians. The following section gives first a rather detailed account of Siddha *materia medica* and its use, and moves on to the cure prescribed for a number of various diseases. Three very brief sections follow: on Siddha yoga, daily regime, and alchemy. The following chapter is concerned with the specific Siddha techniques for the attainment of longevity and 'immortality'. Then follows a description of some doctrinal aspects of Siddhism as reflected in contemporary medical practice, and of a visit in a Siddha dispensary in Madras. Tantrik Siddha school and Siddha attitudes to sex are dealt with next. After the conclusions, a short anthology of selected Siddha poetic texts is offered to the reader. Index of terms in precise transliteration and select bibliography close the book.

2. A Tamil Siddha at Tiruttani

3
On Siddha Medicine

The three systems of indigenous[1] medicine in practice in India at present are Ayurveda, Yunani and Siddha. All three are still very active and, as A. L. Basham has pointed out, although they *may* be 'based in their classical form on *false premises*, are pragmatically effective in curing and relieving many diseases, and their drugs and therapy are less expensive than those of modern Western medicine'.[2] I recognised the truth of these words on my own case in 1968 in Madras.

All three systems are based on humoural pathology which presupposes the same basic physiological doctrine: that air, bile and phlegm (Tamil *vatam, pittam, cilettumam*) are the three main supports of the body; if these three become 'deranged', diseases or death will be the result.

The Siddha system is current in South India, particularly in Tamilnadu and some parts of Karnataka. The word 'Siddha' (in Tamil *cittan*, plural *cittar*) is connected with the Sanskrit word *siddhi* meaning 'accomplishment, complete attainment (of some object)', in particular 'the acquisition of supernatural powers by magical means or the

---

1 I use the term 'indigenous' in this context not as implying that these systems are all of Indic origin, but to indicate traditional Indian systems in contrast to modern Western medicine. Among the three, the Hindu Ayurveda is almost totally autochthonous, and so is apparently the Siddha system, whereas Yunani is originally Perso-Arabic.

2 A. L. Basham (ed.), *A Cultural History of India* , Oxford, 1975, p. 493.

supernatural faculty so acquired'. The designation 'Siddha', in the meaning of 'perfected, accomplished, endowed with supernatural faculties' refers to different groups and classes of beings: it is a term used for inferior Hindu deities, said to possess eight supernatural faculties; it is also a name of a sect in North India partly synonymous with *natha*;[3] in Buddhism, it denotes a class of saints who have attained *siddhi* or perfection in Tantrik rites; in Jainism, this term is equivalent to the designation *tirthankara*.[4] However, in the context of South Indian Tamil culture, the Siddhas (*cittar*) are those who have attained the eight great supernatural powers, use their achievement in medical cure and/or alchemy, and express their views and doctrine in prose and verse composed in Tamil. Another, and simpler definition of Tamil Siddhas simply is 'a class of popular writers in Tamil on all branches of knowledge', including medicine, magic and alchemy (most often, the borderline among these three is very vague indeed). However, I find this simplified definition too general, not specific enough.

Seen from a historical perspective, at least three groups of thinkers bear the designation Siddha in Tamil culture:[5]

1) A group of alchemists and physicians who have constituted the indigenous school of medicine, and composed a (probably vast) number of alchemical and medical treatises, as yet almost unknown to outsiders, whether Indian or non-Indian. This group constitutes the *citta vaittiyam* or 'Siddha medicine' and *citta racavatam* or 'Siddha alchemy'.

2) A group of esoteric poets who have composed a large volume of poetry in Tamil between roughly the 10th - 15th centuries AD.

3) A few 'Siddha-like' mystical poets who have been classed with the Siddha thinkers by later generations, or who called themselves *cittar* without properly belonging (so it would seem) to the esoteric group mentioned above (e.g. Tayumanavar of the 17th century, or Ramalinga Svami, 1823 - 1874).

Siddhis are powers either attained by birth (as the result of previous merit, earlier positive *karma*), or by alchemical means, by power of words (*mantra*), or by mortification coupled with proper training and

---

3 *Natha*, lit. 'lord', name of a Yogic-Tantrik cult especially in Northern India; cf. e. g. B. Walker, *Hindu World* , London, 1968, Vol. 2. , 128.

4 *Tirthankara* , the usual name of the 24 salvation-preachers or chief saints of Jainism of whom the last (Mahavira) was a historical person.

5 Cf. K. V. Zvelebil, *The Poets of the Powers* , London, 1973, p. 17.

thorough concentration. Let me say at once that, unbelievable as these claims may sound, I was at least once witness to some of these faculties. Usually eight great powers (*asta macitti*) are enumerated:

1. *animan* or 'shrinking' - the faculty to reduce oneself to the size of an atom;

2. *mahiman* or 'illimitability' - the power of increasing one's size without limit;

3. *laghiman* or 'lightness' - the power of becoming light as wool and float in the air;

4. *gariman* or 'weight' - the power of rendering the body immaterial and penetrate matter;

5. *prakamya* or 'irresistible will' - the ability to overcome natural obstacles;

6. *isitva* or 'supremacy' - the supreme dominion over body and mind, animate and inanimate nature;

7. *vasitva* or 'dominion over the elements' - the ability to change the course of nature and assuming any form;

8. *kamavasayitva* or 'fulfilment of desires' - the power of attaining anything desired.

However, a true Siddha is supposed to overcome the temptation of these *siddhis*.

The Siddha medical system claims to be original, not derived from the ancient Indian Ayurveda. Various mythical or legendary figures are credited with its origin, foremost among them Nandisa, the companion of Siva - the god's white bull, a theriomorphic form of the deity - and Agastya (Tamil Akattiyar); he is credited to have performed the trephination of the skull of his pupil Teraiyar, removing a large toad (*terai*) from his brain. Incidentally, some of the medical treatises ascribed to Akattiyar contain fascinating details: thus his *Kurunaticcuttiram* mentions seminal animalcules, discovered in the West by Ludwig Hamm only in 1677.[6] According to another legend, Auvaiyar, the famous ancient lady-poet, in the times of Akattiyar, had two sons, Iramatevar and Yakkopu (obviously Yakob, Yakub) who were the true initiators of the Tamil Siddha medical system. My own Tamil Siddha informant in

---

[6] Cf. Robert's *Oriental Illustrations of the Sacred Scriptures* , p. 281, *English Encyclopaedia*, Biography, Vol. III, p. 87; Taylor, W., *Oriental Historical Manuscripts* I, pp. 135, 172, 175, *Madras Journal of Literature and Science*, Vol. IX, p. 161 (Brown).

Madras in 1968-69 claimed descent from the lineage (*parampara*) of Yakkopu.

The literature on the Tamil Siddhas as poets is still very meagre.[7] The literature on the Tamil Siddha physicians of old in any other language than Tamil is even thinner.[8] In Tamil, there are a few original medical treatises which are usually a mixture of pharmacopoeia, diagnostics, alchemy, magic, therapy, mythology, metaphysics, Yoga and poetry. Only lately, a few papers have been published in English by several Western-educated Siddha practitioners. However, one must not forget that the Siddha *vaidya* (medicine) is an *esoteric skill*, and a part of the largely *secret* Yogic-alchemical folklore - hence a tradition of healing practice transmitted *orally* from master to student, generation after generation, without most of it ever having been written down.

What may be more or less openly discussed is not so much the pharmacology and the therapeutic processes and practices as rather the doctrinal culture, the ideological basis of the therapeutic, pharmacological and alchemical practice. Nevertheless, I was singularly lucky to acquire personal co-operation of a Siddha informant who was a practicing Siddha physician (*vaidya, vaittiyan*). In 1968, while on a study trip to Madras, I suffered from a particularly vicious and stubborn attack of dysentery which was cured fast and effectively by a Siddha physician. He became my first informant, and most of my data concerning the practice of Tamil Siddha alchemy and medicine come from him and his confrères whom I met subsequently, between 1968 - 69 (although I had some meagre notions on Siddha *vaittiyam* even in 1967, and in fact during my very first field-trip to India in 1958 and 1959). I was guided to some Siddha texts published in Tamil, and to a few practicing Siddha

---

7 Cf. A. V. Subramania Aiyar, *The Poetry and Philosophy of the Tamil Siddhars, An Essay in Criticism*, Tirunelveli, 1957; Chidambaram, 1969; Kamil V. Zvelebil, *The Poets of the Powers*, London, 1973 (repr. Integral Publishing, 1993; also an Italian edition, *I maestri dei poteri*, Ubaldini Editore, Roma, 1979); D. Buck, 'The Snake in the Song of a Sittar', *Structural Approaches to South India Studies* , 1974, pp. 162 - 83.

8 Cf. Karaiccittar, *Golden Lay*, Madras, Siddhasram, 1960; Shanmuga Velan, A., *Siddhars' Science of Longevity and Kalpa Medicine of India*, Madras, 1963; Kamil V. Zvelebil, 'The Ideological Basis of the Siddha Search for Immortality', *South Asian Digest of Regional Writings*, Vol. 8 (1979) 1-9; Daniel, E. Valentine, 'The Pulse as an Icon in Siddha Medicine', *Contributions to Asian Studies*, Leiden, 18, 1984, 115 - 26.

alchemists and physicians, notably to Sri Balaramiah, Sri Venugopal, Sri Shanmugavelu, and a few others.[9]

The traditions, ideology, practices and literature of the Siddhas represent one of the most perplexing and fascinating pages in the history of Indian civilisation. Siddha writings are at once most thrilling, even sensational but at the same time the darkest and only very little-known texts in Tamil. They represent a complex and provocative puzzle: flashes of stunning intuition, knowledge, even deep wisdom as well as results of effective practice seem to be mixed with incredible naiveté, hardly acceptable superstitions, and dark and amazing claims.

One of the most thrilling and attractive features of Siddha writings is their revolutionary social outlook as well as their iconoclastic attitude towards the Indian Hindu 'establishment' (particularly when it comes to the sexual sphere, or to such institutions as the caste system).

The Siddhas claim to have achieved surprising psychokinetic powers and other capabilities belonging to the sphere of parapsychological phenomena. They even claim that 'death can be dodged, if not wiped out'. They speak of the 'art of deathlessness'; they maintain that the great pre-modern Tamil poet, Ramalinga Svami (1823 - 1874) was one of them, and that he has never died.[10] Those of them who are aware of the history of Western thought claim among their kin the famous German sage Paracelsus (1493 - 1541). Siddha texts speak of incredible feats, and one may legitimately ask whether such claims represent mad bragging of deranged minds, or whether they are based on some experimental

---

9 How I got first acquainted with the Tamil Siddhas is briefly described in the first chapter ('The Personal Account') of my 1973 (1993) book. In subsequent years, I studied the Siddha texts and poetry, and the present volume is thus the outcome of a study commenced seriously in 1968 and going in an 'on and off' manner during the following 25 years, when my much more demanding teaching duties and claims of strict research into Dravidian linguistics and literary history prevented me from a systematic investigation of the Tamil Siddha phenomenon.

10 One day early in 1874 Ramalinga is reported to have had himself locked in a room in Mettukkuppam (which he used for his deep meditations) and instructed his disciples not to open it for some time. He has never been seen since. After some time the room was opened by British administrators, and when they found no one there, it was again locked and sealed. For Ramalinga, cf. G. Vanmikanathan, *Pathway to God trod by Saint Ramalingar* , Bharatiya Vidya Bhavan, Bombay, 1976.

grounds; or - a third alternative - whether these utterings are only reflections of symbolic language, intended to cover some other hidden meanings.

Finally, a word about a particular type of Siddha obscenity. Our Western sensibility may be (and indeed often was) offended by what had been described as vulgar, coarse and obscene features of some expressions of Indian Hindu art (sculpture, painting) and literature. Even Indians themselves, when raised on the niceties of early 20th century English or Anglo-Indian culture, described the Siddhas as 'plagiarists and impostors', 'eaters of opium and dwellers in the land of dreams, their conceit knowing no bounds' (M. Srinivasa Aiyangar, 1914).[11] The obscenity of Siddha writings is twofold. One, it is usually coupled with the expression of disgust, or part of superlative hyperboles, as when The Siddha with the Dancing Snake exclaims, 'We can change men into women and pricks into cunts'; or when Pattinattar speaks of the stinking chasms of the vulva, of 'a cunt wherein . . . crawl flies and ants', and of his own body 'full of lust and lechery' with its 'towering weapon swelling into skies'. Or, indeed, in case of Tantrik-oriented Siddhas (a minority but certainly not negligible), the meticulous descriptions and instructions concerning sexual organs and ritual coitus must be taken as part of a 'technical' know-how of what is in fact a very serious, maybe deadly serious matter. We must never forget that the Siddhas' obscenity has nothing whatsoever pornographic in it; it is never obscene for obscenity's sake, or to arouse lust. The present book is an attempt to approach the Siddha teachings, thought and practice in a sound, critical yet sympathetic manner.

---

11 In *Tamil Studies* (Madras, 1914), p. 226. The book, dedicated to 'The Honourable Sir Harold Stuart . . . Member of Council, Madras', is rather valuable. To be just to it, one should mention that, although its author describes the language of the Siddhas as 'slang', he warns the reader not to mistake their religion for atheism, and has some objective and positive words to say about them (117 - 28).

4

The Ideological Basis Of Siddha Quest For Immortality

The basic axiom of the specifically Siddha approach to life-and-death is this: Whereas it is usually and generally believed that liberation (*mukti*) from the cycle of birth-and-death, and the release from the thraldom of matter, can be achieved by leaving behind the body as a corpse, i.e. *post mortem*, after physical death, according to the Siddhas, such position is a reflection of outright ignorance (*avidya*). While the non-Siddha proclaims that, in order to escape 'the wheel of birth-and-death' the only course open to man is the attainment of spiritual freedom crowned by physical, bodily death, the Siddha maintains that one must overcome physical death in this life itself and 'live forever'. This means that special techniques are available to human beings to attain release from the thraldom of matter while still in flesh, and that from that moment on one is a deathless monad, untouched by the laws of normal biological economy.

According to the Siddhas man has five-fold body (*deha*): a triune natural body, and a double spiritual body. The triune natural body of man is formed of impure matter, and is classifiable into gross or 'dark' body (Tamil *irul tekam*), subtle body (Tamil *marul tekam*) still governed by delusion, and supersubtle or pure body (Tamil *cutta tekam*), divine but perceptible. The fourth body is the *pranava tekam* or non-perceptible body, which is visible but not perceptible by touch, and indestructible. The fifth and final body is the *nanatekam* or immortal body, invisible and all-pervasive.[1]

The gross body (*irul tekam*) is the outgrowth of the subtle (*marul*), and the subtle of the supersubtle (*cuttam*). The transmigrational circuit, when thorough, cleanses the essence of the triune body of its dross of impurity, telescoping the less subtle into the more subtle. But this riddance of impurity from the united body induced by transmigrational cleansing is still incomplete. A special method must be devised for bringing the purified but corruptible matter of the natural body completely into line with the incorruptible and naturally pure matter (*cutta mayai*) with a view to free the human body from the demands made upon it by the scheme of biological economy. The intervention of the Siddha is at this moment essential; unless the triune body of *asuddha maya* (corruptible matter) is transformed into a body of *suddha maya* (pure matter), death and transmigration cannot be avoided. When the transmutation of the *asuddha* into the *suddha maya* has been accomplished under the guidance of a Siddha, the body becomes incorruptible and cannot be affected by death: such body is the *pranava tekam* (i. e. body consisting of the *pranava* syllable *om*), and the carrier of such body is known as *jivan mukta*, liberated while in this life, for he is in touch with both the world of impure matter and the realm of pure spirit or Mind. The relationship with the world of impure matter is only of short duration, for such person is on his/her way to the realm of pure spirit, and when he/she achieves the final 'body' termed *nanatekam* (i. e. body of knowledge, spiritual body), he/she takes leave of the world of

---

1 The preceding text is in many respects indebted to a treatise by a contemporary Siddha, V. Balaramiah (Vaidya Ratnam), entitled *The Art of Deathlessness* (Madras, 1974). - The gross body is termed also *stula sariram* (< Sanskrit) or *paruvutal* (Tamil); the subtle body is also termed *cuksma cariram* or *nunnutal* ; and the supersubtle body is termed *karanacariram* or *karanavutal*.

matter, pure and impure, and suddenly disappears with his/her body into thin air.

Consequently, according to the Siddha view, the human body must in any event be purified and transmuted, i.e. made eternally into one with life in the most uncompromising sense, if death and the 'wheel of rebirth' are to be prevented. Body (*mey*) and life-force (*uyir*) must become *absolutely* identical, totally one, proof against any liability to their mutual separation known to us as 'death'. Thus the great work that lies before man is to purify one's body and sanctify one's life, and integrate the two (i.e. body, *mey*, and life-essence, *uyir*) into one eternal monad, so that body and life become identical. Curiously but interestingly enough, the methods and techniques of attaining such a state include in their component of physico-psychic culture the use of sex, and of such body substances like sperm, discharge from female sexual organs during intercourse (*curata nir* 'coition-secretion'), or amniotic fluid. This feature of Siddha techniques is connected with the influence of Saktism and Tantrism - i.e. with visualising the male as the 'passively creative' Siva and his female partner as Siva's *sakti*.

The key to the method and disciplines wherewith 'to kill death' is to be obtained by an elaborate process which I shall try to outline. This process is summarily known in Tamil as *kaya citti* (binding of body and life together).

1. It begins with a purifying cure of the cells, tissues and organs of the body by rigidly ordered life-style based chiefly on alimentary restrictions, and also by concurrent practice of yoga, of interior prayer aimed at setting up unique molecular vibrations in the body that ought ultimately to bring about its specific composition, and, in addition, with Tantrik-oriented Siddhas, of ritual coitus. The techniques to achieve this are both physiological and mental. Both are covered by the term *muppu*. As mental/spiritual techniques, *muppu* designates esoteric interior prayer, obtained from a guru of the Siddha *marga*. In other words, one must find a spiritual guide among the Siddhas and learn the secret of interior prayer directly from him. In this sense, *muppu* is described by the saying *nalla maruntu, ennul irukkum maruntu, nanamaruntu* (i.e. 'The excellent medicine, medicine which is inside me, medicine of *nanam* '). However, *muppu* in the second sense, physiological or physical, is more controversial and more interesting; it is said to give health and longevity. Even among the present practicing Siddha physicians, this is a matter of heated controversy, for they have each their own *vaittiya muppu*, i.e.

inherited, 'secret' medicines playing an important role in the regeneration of cells and the neutralization of the effects of exotoxins and foreign bodies.

2. The processes just mentioned tend to bring about the appearance of new tissues and regenerated organs and functions in place of the old ones, allowed to pass away through disuse, inanition and marasmus.

3. Next, by virtue of a systematic physio-psychic and psycho-spiritual culture of a special kind, the regenerate visible body, and later also its companions, the 'subtle' body and the 'supersubtle' body are reduced to their radical conformations in order to telescope the least subtle of these bodies into the less subtle, and the less subtle into the subtle, so that, ultimately, the process results in the *dematerializing transmutation* of the refined though perishable physical basis of life into a trans-physical, incorruptible, everlasting one. The contrast between matter and mind, matter and consciousness disappears; mind and matter appear as mutually enfolding projections of a higher reality which is neither matter nor consciousness.[2]

The modus of the transmutation of the corruptible into the incorruptible body is, of course, in its essence preternatural and mystical, although initially it has to do with an ultra-organic sublimitation of the previously cleansed somatic constituents. During the process of the transmutation or 'transubstantiation', a very important role is given to a material, a drug (*maruntu*) called *muppu*, the Tamil Siddha equivalent of

---

2 In this connection, it is interesting to call to mind the words of Noam Chomsky (*The Listener*, 30 May 1968) who says, 'The concept of "physical" has been extended step by step to cover anything we understand', so that 'when we ultimately begin to understand the properties of mind, we shall simply. . . extend the notion "physical" to cover these properties as well.' Since these words were uttered, philosophy of science has moved forward by giant steps, and in the works of such eminent physicists as Sir John C. Eccles, Henry Margenau or David Bohm (and others) we witness the disappearance of the 'classic', traditional dichotomy of mind and matter, 'soul' and body. In fact, we have seen, during the last twenty or thirty years, the demise of basic tenets of materialism, both in physics and in biology. Cf. such publications as K. Popper and J. Eccles, *The Self and Its Brain* (1975), H. Margenau, *The Nature of Physical Reality* (1977), J. Eccles, *The Human Mystery* (1979), L. LeShan and H. Margenau, *Einstein's Space and Van Gogh's Sky* (1982), H. Margenau, *The Miracle of Existence* (1987).

the 'elixir of life',[3] i.e. to *muppu* in its second meaning quoted. According to some of my informants, it is a kind of inorganic drug, composed probably of mercury, sulphur and salt. However, I regard this information as an oversimplification or, perhaps, deliberate misinformation. It would rather seem that under the term *muppu* the Siddhas include a number of complex organic catalysts which can increase or diminish the velocity of a reaction or participate in the promotion of the end-products of a reaction. We are here at the very heart of Siddha *vaidya*, and hence I shall deal with *muppu* in some detail, although I must warn the readers that almost all I have to say about it is probably rather tentative and most probably incomplete (cf. also further on).

Two large classes of *muppu* are distinguished by the Siddhas (or, rather, I should say by those Siddhas willing to open up): one class is the soluble *muppu* which may be extracted from tissues, and which includes substances produced in the body as specific antitoxins. According to some informants, these substances may be extracted in particular from urine, saliva, blood and sperm. This kind of *muppu* is termed *civakutinir muppu*, lit. the *muppu* which is the liquid drunk by Siva (another term is *pintamuppu*, lit. embryo-*muppu*, and may indeed refer to placental liquid). The second class of *muppu* is not developed in the body but is believed to be the simplest organic substance which is the beginning stage of the development of every living organism in the universe. It is termed *antamuppu*, lit. the egg (but also 'testicle' or 'seed') *muppu* or else *punir muppu*, i. e. the *muppu* [found as] water [in] the earth.[4] It is maintained that this primeval organic matter develops in marshy ground on full moon days in the months of January through April.

Another classification of *muppu* may be found in some Siddha texts, particularly those ascribed to the famous Pokar (Bhoga); this is the division into *yoka muppu, vata muppu* and *vaittiyamuppu*. *Yoka muppu* is

---

3 This material is termed differently in different Siddha lineages, e. g. *nanapintu, antakkal, sivamsakti, natam-pintam*, but the most frequent term is *muppu*, or *amirtam* (<Sanskrit *a-mrta-* 'im-mortal').

4 *Punir* is also sometimes etymologized as 'the water of the flower' (Tamil *pu*). Nonetheless, the derivation 'earth water' seems to me to be more probable (Tamil *pu* < Sanskrit *bhu-* 'earth') since, in folk-medicine, and in the practice of some less sophisticated Siddha physicians, a crude whitish - grey clay, gathered, dried and mixed with dew or rain-water, is used as *muppu* of the *punir* kind.

that kind of substance which develops in the body due to constant practice of *astanga yoga*, the eightfold Yoga. Modern-oriented Siddha practitioners explain these substances as hormones, enzymes, antibodies and antitoxins which retard the degeneration of the cells and thus prolong life.

Akattiyar (of unknown date) states that this *muppu* may be obtained by collecting the amniotic fluid (*paninir*) of the primipara (i.e. the fluid in which an unborn foetus floats in the amnion of a woman giving birth for the first time) into a golden vessel and dried in the hot sun. A white amorphous substance will crystallize in the bowl which according to Akattiyar contains sex hormones, a combination of *natam* (female 'semen') and *vintu* (male seed), having rejuvenating and life-prolonging properties. In this connection, I would like to mention again the use (by oral intake) of substances like prostatic secretion, male sperm, and so-called female semen (i.e. pre-coital and orgasmic discharge) recommended by some Siddha physicians, ancient and contemporary. In particular, the mixed male sperm and female coital discharge being licked immediately after coitus is beleived to be particularly invigorating. All this has obviously to do with physiological manifestations pertaining to generative organs, procreation and origin of life.

As to *vatamuppu*, it is very difficult to understand what is meant exactly by this substance; *vatam* 'utterance, speech' in this context means the *paribhasa*, the secret professional jargon of the alchemists, and *vatamuppu* can most probably be regarded either as the Siddha equivalent of the Western 'philosopher's stone', or as mantra.[5]

Vaittiya muppu (*vaittiyam* < *vaittyam* < Sanskrit *vaidya*- 'medicine') are substances used in the preparation of Siddha drugs. They are described in detail in specific manuals of Siddha *vaidya*, and every Siddha physician has his own *vaittiya muppu*'s either as traditionally inherited drugs, or uses the ones mentioned in handbooks of Siddha pharmacopoeia published in Tamil. I have for instance been given the following fascinating prescription: Dissolve alcalic (potash)

---

5 I could not obtain any definitive information regarding this kind of *muppu*. One informant maintained that it is nothing else but common salt (*vatamaiyuppu*). However, *vatam* is a frequent abbreviation for *(i)racavatam* 'alchemy'.

washerman's or fuller's earth[6] in rain / dew water; strain on the third day, dry in the heat of the sun, add salt in lumps, stone-lime and powdered skull-bone with camphor, stir with a silver spoon - and the resulting powder ('salt') is *muppu* to be used *per os* against various diseases. In the following chapters I shall deal in considerable detail with drugs and prescriptions.

To return to the process of the transmutation of the body. It is said that a body which has been rendered incorruptible does not cast shadows, does not leave footprints, cannot be felt by touch, or even pierced by sword. It is known as *pranavatanu*, i.e. body equivalent to the sacred most mantra *om*.[7] When I demanded some more information on this incorruptible, transfigured body, I was to my amazement reminded of the hypothesis of the existence of anti-matter, and of anti- particles, which had been theoretically predicted by the British Nobel Prize winner Paul A. M. Dirac in 1927, and which appears to have been experimentally proven by the production of anti-helium-3 by Russian physicists (Yuri Prokoshkin at Serpukhov near Moscow about two decades ago). Since I am completely incompetent critically to judge, approve or reject such awesome matters as anti-matter, I leave it at that, and proceed with the Siddha path to perfection.

The absolutely final consummation of the whole process of this spiritual alchemy is not the transmuted *pranavatanu* but the eternal spiritual body called *tivyatanu* ('divine body'), an entity outside the range of human gaze and experience. Only then the individual *paramukta* and the eternal cosmic life-substance enter into inseparable unity, and final and total release results. Hence, the initial sine qua non of the final release is not physical death but dematerialization, transubstantiation of the body, and therein consists the most specific feature of the Siddha quest of immortality and eternal youth.

Though the spiritually freed man has the capacity to lead an infinitely long life of perpetual youth in his death-proof body, he does not usually choose to do so. The moment he should normally die he disappears with his transfigured subtle body with no indication as to his future whereabouts. We may well ask whether we know of a case of such

---

6 'Fuller's earth' is a variety of clay-like materials which absorb oil and grease and are used in scouring textiles and in refining oils and fats.

7 Other terms used to designate this body are *mantratanu* and *baindavasarira* (i. e. body composed of the *bindu*).

mysterious disappearance. Indeed we do. The well-known Ramalinga Svami (1823 - 1874), one of the great Tamil poets of the 19th century, is reported to have been locked in a room which he used for his meditations (at Mettukkuppam near Madras) and never been seen since. The date was Friday, Jan. 30, 1874. The passing of Ramalinga created a stir and gave rise to various rumours so that the authorities decided to look into the matter. In May of 1874, Mr. J. H. Garstin, I. C. S., Collector of South Arcot, and Mr. G. Banbury, I. C. S., a member of the Board of Revenue, visited Ramalinga's single-room house. In their presence the room was opened, and it was empty. Finding nothing incriminating, the two Englishmen donated twenty rupees for the feeding of the poor and left.[8]

To sum up: Life cannot exist without form, and form implies the possession of a body. Birth is one modus operandi of life's embodiment or manifestation, death of life's disembodiment or rejection of an old form. As long as there is need for the renewal of form, life must continue to wander through the realm of matter, putting on ever new forms and rejecting old ones. Final release from this transmigratory whirlpool can be achieved only through the annihilation of bodily death because through death one always slips anew into the transmigratory process. A Siddha is one who has attained the power to pass into the Unseen, when his moment has come, not by the portal of bodily death but by vanishing into space because his body is a transmuted body, so ethereal in composition that death cannot touch it. Put in a different way, his body and 'soul' (life) have become an inseverable, homogenous whole.

When evaluating ideologically this entire process of perfection as outlined in the Siddha speculation, the key to understanding such approach may possibly be found in the following remark by Carl Gustav Jung: 'The eastern mind. . . has no difficulty in conceiving of a consciousness without an ego. Consciousness is deemed capable of transcending its ego condition; indeed, in its higher form, the ego disappears altogether.'

Lately, several scientists have come up with a hypothesis presupposing the existence of what they termed Shadow Matter. It seems that the first to formulate this in an articulate way was E. W. Kolb *et al.*

---

8 Cf. P. Balakrishnan, 'Ramalinga, Poet and Prophet', *JSAL* XIX (2), Summer-Fall 1984, p. 24.

in 1985.[9] Subsequently, a coherent theory has been built up on this hypothesis by G. D. Wassermann who argues that man consists of an ordinary matter body and, in addition, a Shadow Matter body which includes a Shadow Matter brain. After death of the ordinary matter body the Shadow Matter body and its Shadow Matter brain could live on, possibly indefinitely ('ignoring' the second law of thermodynamics). Without attempting any discussion of the plausibility of this theory I only wish to point out that in some aspects it strikingly resembles the ideas put forward by Tamil Siddhas as described in this chapter.[10]

3. A Siddha at Vallimalai (Northwest of Madras)

---

[9] Kolb, E. W., Seckel, D. and Turner, M. S. (1985), 'The shadow world of superstring theories', *Nature* (London) 314, 415 - 19.

[10] Cf. Gerhard D. Wassermann, *Shadow Matter and Psychic Phenomena*, Mandrake, Oxford, 1993.

5
Basic Tenets Of Siddha Medicine

In 1973, when my first book appeared on the Tamil Siddhas, I wrote that I was not 'competent enough to deal with the subject' of *cittavaittiyam* or Siddha medicine 'in any appreciable detail'.[1] Since then, mainly due to the study of Siddha texts both in Tamil and - to a much lesser extant for they are only very few - in English, as well as to several subsequent trips to Tamilnadu, I feel more confident than at that time to discuss the subject.

There is both a historical and a logical reason to the Siddha claim that the physical body must be preserved as long as possible, and in as good a condition as possible. The historical reason is to be sought in the general development of Indian thought in late post-Upanishadic period, when the pessimism and asceticism of the Upanishads and of early Buddhism gave way to a more positive attitude towards one's body as found in early Hindu and classical periods and in Buddhist Mahayana: the human body becomes a reliable and effective instrument of man in the quest for contentment and happiness in this life in the two main spheres of human activity - in mating and in fighting, in love and in conquest; and in his quest of liberation, his quest to conquer bondage and death. The logical

---

1 *Op. cit.* p. 31.

reason stems from the idea that liberation can be achieved in this very life; hence, the body must be preserved as an aid to meditation leading to freedom. Spiritual development towards liberation being much slower than physical changes, the ageing of the body must be delayed. To achieve full development of body and mind, the Siddha must hold back time. And to be able to know how to do it, he needs certain methods and techniques: a particular sort of Yoga, alchemy and *cittavaittiyam* (Siddha medicine).

According to my main Siddha informant, fifty-five years of age is the prime of life, and old age as in the West we know it need not come at all to one who has learned how to arrest physiological age and to some extent even to reverse it.[2]

The spiritual ancestor of the Siddhas, Tirumular (6th - 7th cent. A.D.) says in his *Tirumantiram* 661:

> For those who know
> there is *no* going and *no* coming,
> there is *no* death and *no* birth.

And one of the Siddhas, the Siddha With the Earthen Ring, Kutampai Cittar,[3] speaks of 'those who walk the Unique Path of mastering completely deathlessness'; they are those 'who have beaten well nigh the god of death'.

Probably one of the most forceful and explicit traditional statements in verse-form about the necessity to take care of one's body to achieve immortality of the soul occurs again in Tirumular's[4] *Tirumantiram* 704-5:

> Those who let the body decay, destroy the spirit;
> and they won't attain the powerful knowledge of truth.
> Having learned the skill of fostering the body
> I fostered the body, and I nurtured the soul.
>
> Formerly I thought that the body was foul.

---

2 *Op. cit.* p. 32.

3 For this Siddha, cf. my 1973 (1993) book, pp. 111-12.

4 For more information on Tirumular cf. below, and also pp. 72-80 of my 1973 (1993) publication.

I saw that there was Ultimate Reality within the body.
The Perfect One has entered the temple of the body.
I protected and preserved my body.

There are a few key ideas and terms in these well-known stanzas which should be stressed. There is, in Tamil, an important homonymy of the key term *mey*[5] which means both 'body' and 'truth' and 'reality'. When Tirumular speaks of the powerful knowledge of truth (*titampata mey-n-nanam*) he speaks because of this homonymy at the same time about the powerful knowledge of the body. This is one of the basic code-words to understand Siddha thought: true knowledge, knowledge of *truth is* knowledge of and about the *body*. Tirumular (regarded as one of the greatest saints, Yogins and Siddhas) has learned the *upaya* of fostering the body. This is another technical term of utmost importance: a Sanskrit word meaning 'way, stratagem, craft, artifice, skillful means'. By nurturing and fostering the body, Tirumular has learned how to protect, nourish and foster *uyir*; another polyvalent term meaning 'life, breath, soul, spirit'.

The *first* basic tenet of Siddha medicine is the vision of man as an integral part of universal nature. The natural forces acting in and through the various organs of human body are closely related to, and in fact, integrated into corresponding forces acting in and through cosmic structures. In one of his philosophical poems, the Siddha Cattaimuni[6] says: The body exists within the universe; the universe and the body are one; the universe exists within the body; *this* is true knowledge.

Just as, in the great cosmic organism, these forces may act abnormally and thereby bring about cosmic diseases (like earthquakes and other natural catastrophes), they may act in an abnormal manner in bodily organism, and cause various illnesses.

Closely connected with this general principle is the notion that every sign of the Zodiac has an aspect vis-à-vis some part of the human body, and that planets exert great influence over human organism.

---

5 Cf. *Dravidian Etymological Dictionary (Revised)* 5073.

6 Supposed to have been a Siddha physician living in the time of Akastiyar (hence semi-legendary). Of weaver community. Said also to have been disciple of Pokar. Ascribed to him : *Cattaimuni nanam, Tirikantam, Carakkuvaippu, Navarattinavaippu.*

To quote the most often occurring instances of the relationship between the signs of the Zodiac and body parts: Aries relates to the neck; Libra to the kidneys; Taurus to the shoulders; Scorpio to the genitals; Gemini to arms and hands; Sagittarius to hips; Cancer to the chest; Capricorn to the knees; Leo to the heart and stomach; Aquarius to the legs; Virgo to intestines; Pisces to the feet.

Planets exercise special power over body by causing diseases according to their influence on the three humours.

Mercury presides over legs, feet, arms, hands, fingers, tongue, nerves and ligaments, and can cause epilepsy, convulsions etc.

Venus presides over throat, breasts, abdomen, genitalia, semen, taste, smell etc. , and can produce barrenness as well as death from sexual excess, but also abscesses and gonorrhoea.

Mars has power over gall-bladder (hence bile), kidneys, pudenda, etc., and can cause jaundice, haemorrhage, ulcers, etc.

Jupiter presides over liver, veins (hence blood), diaphragm, sense of touch, while

Saturn has jurisdiction over bones, teeth, ear, spleen, brain, and may give rise to leprosy, cancer, cough, asthma etc.

The *second* basic tenet of Siddha medicine is connected with the question of what constitutes human body - in other words, with the theory of the ninety-six *tattvas*[7] and other constituent body elements. The human body is composed - in addition to other constituents - of these ninety-six *tattvas* which include so called 'powers of the soul' (*attuma tattuvam*, nos. 1-5 in our list) as well as nerves, organs of perception, faculties etc.

1. *aim putam* or Five elements (see below, the third basic tenet).
2. *aim pulan* or Five sense organs (of taste, sight, touch, hearing and smell).
3. *karumentiriyam* or Five organs of motor action.
4. *nanentiriyam* or Five organs of perception.
5. *antakkaranam* or Four aspects or faculties (of thought, feeling, volition and sense of ego).
6. *taca nati*: Ten (main) nerves.

7 *Tattva* (Sanskrit 'true/real state', literally 'truth, reality') is in this context to be understood as primordial, basic essence.

7. *pancavastai* alias *aintavattai* or Five (main) psychological states (or conditions of the embodied soul, referring to watchfulness, sleep etc.).
8. *mummalam*: three impurities of the soul which cling to it until it attains final liberation.
9. *mukkunam*: three (basic) qualities (of excellence or virtue, pride or arrogance, and darkness or sluggishness).
10. *muppini*: the three humours - wind, bile and phlegm (cf. the fourth basic tenet).
11. *munru mantalam*: the three regions (sun, moon and fire).
12. *en vikaram*: the eight predominant passions.
13. *arataram*: the six *cakras* or dynamic tattvic centres which represent the nerve plexuses of the body (Yoga).
14. *eluvakai tatu*: the seven constituent elements of the body.
15. *taca vayu*: the ten vital airs.[8]
16. *panca kocam*: the five cases or sheaths of the soul.
17. *onpatu vacal*: the nine 'doors' or vents of the body.

The concept of these *tattvas*[9] is certainly nothing specific for Tamil Siddha ideology. It has been adopted and adapted from other Hindu schools of thought. What is of concern to us when it comes to Siddha medicine is the teaching about the five elements (third basic tenet), the three humours (fourth basic tenet), and the six *cakras* which play an enormous role in Siddha Yoga.

The Siddha school has added to the ninety-six *tattvas* the notion that the human body is also composed of 72,000 blood- vessels, 13,000 nerves, ten main arteries, ten vital airs, and that it is liable - due to the derangement of the three humours - to 4448 diseases!

The *third* basic principle of Siddha medicine is concerned with the relationship of the five elements to the human body. These five elements are defined as earth (*pirutivi*), water (*appu*), fire (*teyu*), wind (*vayu*) and ether (*akacam*). They are found in all bodies in the process of transmutation and union. Here, then, is the sphere of close interrelationship between medicine and alchemy in Siddha thinking.

---

8 Of these, five play an important role in Siddha medicine, see below.

9 Which are in fact variously enumerated as 19, 25, 36 or 96, according to various philosophical schools.

According to this theory, designated as *pancikaranam*, which can be roughly described as the operation of the five elements in the human body by varied unions,[10] he who knows the secrets of *pancikaranam* will understand the hidden qualities of the elements both separately and in combination, and thus bring about some astonishing feats which could be designated as 'miracles'.[11]

The *fourth* basic tenet of Siddha medicine is the notion that almost all diseases are caused by *humoural pathology*. As this is, probably with the science of the pulse, the most important single component of Siddha medical thinking, it must be dealt with in some detail.

Humoural pathology analyses and explains all diseases as caused by relationships among the three cardinal humours, wind, bile and phlegm. These three humours, termed in Tamil *muppini*, represent respectively the air (wind), heat (bile) and water (phlegm) of the five elements which form the connecting link between the microcosm of man (human medicine) and the macrocosm of the universe (alchemy and astronomy/astrology).

The air corresponds to the bodily *vayu* (or *vatam*); the heat corresponds to the internal *pittam*; and the water corresponds to bodily *culettumam*. Man is thus linked with the external world, and any change in the elementary condition of the external world reflects a corresponding change in human organism.

The three humours in their normal order occupy respectively the lower, middle and upper parts of the body maintaining their integrity: *vayu* wind in the regions of pelvis and rectum; *pittam* bile in the regions of stomach and viscera; and *cilettumam* phlegm in the regions of breath, throat and head.

Translating these notions into Western medical science, *vayu* covers the phenomena which relate to sympathetic nervous system, *pittam* to functions of thermogenesis, metabolism, digestion, secretion, excretion, etc., and *cilettumam* to glandular functions, regulation of temperature, and the like. It is further ascertained that all substances of the animal,

---

10 Tantavaraya Cuvamikal's *Kaivalyanavanitam, Tat. 10* (ed. Madras, 1905) defines *pancikaranam* as 'the process of dividing each of the five subtle elements (*cukkuma putankal*) into two equal parts and apportioning one part to its corresponding grosser element (*stula putam*) and one-fourth of the other part to each of the other grosser elements.'

11 I witnessed such a 'miracle' in January 1968 in Madras.

vegetable and mineral realms contain one or more of these humours in their composition. When deranged, the humours cause diseases particular to their influence; when in equilibrium (*camanilai*), freedom from disease.

There is one principle in this teaching which contains a great truth that could and should be incorporated in Western medical practice: according to this principle, no disease can be purely local, isolated, unconnected with other parts and functions of the organism; hence, no disease should be treated in isolation.

The principal rules to be followed in cases of irregularity of the three humours are either to augment the loss or deficiency in order to cure the aggravation, or to try to return the humours to their healthy equilibrium expressed by the following formula:

vayu : pittu : cilettumam = 4 : 2 : 1

In other words, the relation of wind to bile to phlegm equals the proportion of 1 to 1/2 to 1/4. Any change in these proportions is supposed to bring about disease or even death.

We should now examine in detail the part played by each of the three humours in the functioning of the organism, aware of the fact that humoural pathology used to be in vogue among the Greeks, medieval Western alchemists, and even in the Qabalah.

Vayu (alias *vatam* alias *karru*), i. e. wind, present everywhere in the system, all-pervading in its nature, invisible, and yet recognizable by its attributes of touch and sound. It is very prompt in its action, passes through the whole body in rapid currents, and is the root cause of all diseases. But it also forms the life-force (*uyir*) of all animated beings. *Pittam*, bilious humour,[12] produces internal heat, is responsible for metabolism, is the principal agent of digestion and the purging of waste-matter in the form of urine and faeces. Its origin is the liver. In its normal state it remains in bile, in lymph, blood and saliva. Its derangement causes indigestion, jaundice, ulcers, unbearable thirst, sleeplessness, burning sensation in the body, hyperacidity etc.

Cilettumam (< Sanskrit *slesman-*), also *kapam* (< Sanskrit *kapha-*), phlegm, supplies the body with moisture just as *pittam* supplies it with 'heat'. It increases the firmness of limbs, keeping them united and stable.

12 Cf. *pittanir* 'bile', *pittappai* 'gall-bladder'.

It helps digestion, imparts to the tongue the ability to taste, etc. Its derangement causes excess of thirst, dull appetite, throwing out of phlegm in cough, goitre, etc.[13]

The existence of these three humours in the human system in due proportion is well indicated by *pulse*; without its observation, no correct diagnosis is possible. Hence, the science of the pulse represents a very important branch of Siddha medicine (in agreement with its importance in Indian medicine in general).

Pulse means the beating of an artery felt with the tip of the finger or fingers at the wrist, to find out its rate, rhythm and character. In medical practice, this term is usually applied to the beat or throb felt in the radial artery at the wrist, though it may be felt over other arteries as well (carotid, temporal, femoral etc.).

According to Tirumular's work on pulse, the following constituent parts of the human body play an important role in the variation of pulse: *taca vayu* - the ten vital airs; *tiri nati* - the three nerve-channels; *ar-ataram* - the six nerve plexuses; *munru mantalam* - the three regions of the body named the sun, the moon and the fire. The following scheme shows the relationship among various entities to be observed while analyzing a person's pulse:

Humour (tatu)	vatam (wind)	pittam (bile)	aiyam (phlegm)
Vital Air (vayu)	apanan	piranan	camanam
Place of origin (urpatti)	malam faeces	calam water	vintu semen
Region (mantalam)	unti navel	marpu chest	ucci head
Movements (natinatai)	koli fowl	tavalai frog	pampu snake

13 Humoural hypothesis, which is at the base of Siddha therapeutic practice, was ten years ago discussed by Prof. Dr. F. Schwarz (Clinical endocrinology, The University of Utrecht, The Netherlands) in a speech marking the occasion of the 349th Dies natalis, on 26. 3. 1985. See his *Humorale communicatie in het menselijke organisme* (Humoural communication in human organism).

Finger (viral)	atkatti forefinger	natuviral midfinger	motiraviral ringfinger
Measure (mattirai)	1	½	¼

To show how it works, let us interpret the first humour, *vatam* (wind): It results from *apanam*,[14] vital air, centred in the faeces, operating in the lower region of the body up to the navel; it is indicated by the pulse whose movements are compared to the movements of a fowl (*koli*). The beat of this pulse, felt by pressing the forefinger on the radial artery, is taken to be one measure (*mattirai* < Sanskrit *matra-*), as to distinguish it from the other two humours represented by durations of half-a-measure and quarter-measure respectively.

Similarly, one can handle the cases of bile and phlegm. Pulse, according to the Siddhas, is classified into five kinds:

1. *vata nati*, pulse indicating *vatam* or wind humour;
2. *pittanati*, pulse indicating *pittam* or bilious humour;
3. *aiya / cilettumanati*, pulse showing *aiyam / cilettumam* or phlegmatic humour;
4. *putanati*, pulse felt between the thumb and forefinger;
5. *kurunati*, an intermediary pulse (?) felt between fingers.

Another classification of pulse is according to its nature and rate; this is most detailed, but very interesting, and hence it is given here in full:

1. *tiviranati* - fast pulse i. e. faster than normal;
2. *tullunati* - irregular, bouncing, 'goat-leap' pulse;
3. *vannati* - hard or wiry, 'strong' pulse;
4. *apalanati* - weak pulse, with no-strength (*a-palam*);
5. *nerunkiyanati* - tense and firm pulse, 'cord-like';
6. *nirainati* - with copious volume of blood, 'full pulse';
7. *katinati* - characterized by very high tension, 'hard pulse';
8. *tatankunati* - abnormally slow in rate, 'halting pulse';
9. *itaivitunati* - in which various beats are dropped, 'intermittent';
10. *talampunati* - pulse giving the sensation of successive waves,

---

14 *Apanan* (cf. *apanam* < Sanskrit *apana-* 'anus') is one of the *tacavayu* (ten vital airs) : it expels wind, excreta, urine and semen. *Piranan* (< Sanskrit *prana-*) vital air of the body which causes respiration etc.; *camanan* (< Sanskrit *samana-*) vital air of the body which causes digestion.

'undulating';

11. *olunkunati* - pulse beating at normal rate and regularly;
12. *kurnati* - pulse in which the artery is suddenly and markedly distended, 'sharp pulse';
13. *mennati* - pulse in which the force of the beat is very feeble, 'feeble pulse';
14. *tunnati* - nearly imperceptible pulse, 'small pulse';
15. *kampinati* - small tense pulse, 'wiry pulse';
16. *marananati* - jerky pulse with full expansion, followed by sudden collapse, 'deathly pulse';
17. *vikarpanati* - pulse in which strong beats alternate with weak beats, 'unequal pulse';
18. *canninati* - pulse indicating apoplexy (*canni*);
19. *puttamankainati* - pulse showing maturity of a girl, lit. 'pulse of a girl who has [just] menstruated';
20. *otunkunati* - pulse which gradually fades away;
21. *tutinati* - pulse which strikes the finger rapidly, 'abrupt';
22. *utaranati* - pulse which can be seen in emaciated persons over the abdominal aorta, 'abdominal';
23. *irattainati* - pulse in which two beats follow in quick succession, such group of two separated from the following by long interval, 'coupled pulse';
24. *kutiraivottanati* - pulse with small irregular excursions, 'which runs like a horse';
25. *terikkunati* - pulse in which the artery is suddenly and markedly distended, 'jerky pulse'.

Practice: Press three fingers - index, middle and ring finger - of your right hand at a spot two fingers in width just below the root of the thumb. You should feel the pulse three times by holding and letting loose the hand of the patient, and then diagnose the disease with great care and caution.

The natural order in which the forces of the three humours are indicated by the pulse, and are to be observed, is: (1) the pulse showing *vayu* (wind) in the first place above the wrist is felt underneath the forefinger; (2) that of *pittam* (bile) below the middle finger; (3) that of *kappam* (phlegm) under the ring finger. The pulse indicates whether a particular disease is due to *vayu, pittam* or *kapam*, or whether it is due to the combined action of any of two, or to the combined action of all three, or whether, finally, it is caused by some other factors (not *all* diseases are caused by derangement of the three humours, after all!).[15] Finally, the pulse will indicate whether, in principle, the disease is curable or incurable.[16]

The procedure of diagnosis and therapy was set down in India in a well-developed medical theory as early as the sixth century B. C. According to this procedure formulated as four basic questions, one first asked about the symptoms of the disease, then about its cause, then about the possibility of removing that cause, and finally about the medicine(s).[17] The Siddhas also employed sympathetic and adoptive magic in their therapy.

What constitutes according to Siddha tradition a good physician?

First, the physician ought also to be an alchemist or the son of an alchemist (*vati makan vaittiyan*). Saying 'alchemist' read, in fact, 'chemist' (i. e. one who is proficient in the knowledge of matter and the elementary substances to be able to prepare one's own medicines). He should also be a physicist, something of an astronomer (i. e., mainly, astrologer), and philosopher.

Second, a true physician should be able to think original thoughts ('do his own thinking'), and, at the same time, employ intuition and imagination. Also, it is said that a physician who knows nothing else about his patient but what the latter had told him, knows very little indeed (V. Balaramiah).

Third, he should be 'wedded to his art as a man is to his beloved wife', and should love it with all his heart and soul for its own sake, and not for getting rich or famous.

---

15 For various other causes of diseases, see next chapter.

16 For pulse as main diagnostic tool, cf. also Prabhakar Chatterjee, 'Indian Science of Pulse', *College of Ayurveda* Vol. 1, p. XXXVII, 1934; Daniel, E. Valentine, 'The Pulse as an Icon in Siddha Medicine', *Contributions to Asian Studies* (E. J. Brill, Leiden) 18, 1984, 115-26.

17 It is interesting that, apparently, the Buddha followed this (originally medical?) scheme in his formulation of the famous four basic (Aryan, 'Noble') truths, cf. J. W. Schumann, *The Historical Buddha*, Arkana, 1989, p. 57. In this connection, one should recall that the Buddha compared himself to a physician, healing the ill (*dukkha*) of mankind.

Fourth, he must use only medicines which he had prepared himself and not those purchased or borrowed from others.

Further, he should try to relieve his patient from suffering, and on no account delay his treatment in order to extract payments.

Finally, he should not venture to treat a patient without being certain to have arrived at a correct diagnosis.

4. Sculpture of Shakti as mother of creation from Madurai.

6
Diseases And Their Cure

Materia medica - its use

The first thing to do while dealing with Siddha attitudes to diseases and their cure is obviously to itemize the substances which are used in Siddha practice as materia medica. The division of these substances into male substances and female substances reminds us of the Chinese binominal ying-yang speculation.[1] My Siddha informant's opinion was that this division reflected 'modern' knowledge of chemistry, being equivalent to alkaline-based ingredients and to acids.

Most authorities (both in the Tamil written and oral transmission) recognize at least nineteen or twenty[2] basic medical substances which I

---

1 It is possible that the Chinese Taoist alchemists imitated Indian Buddhist-Tantrik teachers, but it is also possible that Tamil alchemy underwent Chinese influence (cf. J. Filliozat, *Journal Asiatique*, CCXXIII, 1963, 110-12, and *Dan Vietnam*, III, Aug. 1949, 113 ff. ; M. Eliade, *Yoga, Immortality and Freedom*, 1969, p. 416).

2 These substances are: waters, milk, oils, cowdung and other kinds of animal ordure, urine, sugar, intoxicants, honey, trees, bushes, creepers, grasses, roots, tubers, spices, salts, stones, metals, nine gems. In addition, some

shall describe in some detail. They are derived from animal, vegetal and mineral realms. This description is based on a voluminous work on materia medica called *Patarttakuna cintamani* (of 1504 stanzas) ascribed to Teraiyar, one of the twelve disciples of Akastiyar.[3]

1. Waters

a. River-water: In general, bathing in the water of rivers is considered healthy (river-bathing in particular, and in fact all bathing in general, is of course an indispensable part of Hindu religiosity). Two Indian rivers are recommended for specific healing properties: Ganges in the North, and Tambiraparani in the South. It is claimed that their waters can even help in cure of many 'incurable' diseases.

b. Water of tanks and ponds: Dangerous! Since it is stagnant and 'polluted' with decaying parts of water-plants like lotus, water-lily etc.

c. Well-water: It is recommended to drink the water from the bottom of wells since that is where the source usually is, whereas the surface-water is usually polluted with fallen leaves etc.

d. Waterfall-water: Bathing under waterfalls strengthens the body.

e. Rice-water (i.e. water in which rice had been boiled, left standing overnight): Prescription: Mix 1 part of rice gruel made from parboiled husked rice with 4 parts of boiled and cooled-off water; pour over a portion of boiled strained rice. Next morning strain, add salt according to taste, drink on empty stomach. Is beneficial in general, helps to cure many diseases. In particular, it makes male sperm fragrant, thick and copious.

f. Juice of banana plant: After felling a banana plant, dig out in the stump of its trunk an opening about 4 inch. deep and 4 inch. wide, put a

---

authorities quote male semen (sperm), menstrual blood, and female discharge before and during intercourse.

3 The work 'has been recently recovered from obscurity through the medium of the Press at Madras, by the laudable industry of Subramanya Panditer . . . We consider that an English translation of this work will no doubt prove a valuable auxiliary to medical men in England in their researches into the Materia Medica of India' (Simon Casie Chitty, *The Tamil Plutarch*, Chilaw, 1859). The original work has been published in print (as ascribed to all the 18 Siddhar) at Culai, 1907. I got acquainted with this all-important work of Teraiyar in its abridged version called *Patartta kuna potini* (Instruction on the Quality of Substances), prepared by a contemporary Siddha researcher, Vi. Palaramayya in 1975.

lid on it (taking care that it remains clean), and leave for 12 hours. The watery juice gathered there, mixed with lime and a bit of borax and put on betel leaf, will stop strangury and dysury, and strengthen the body in general.

g. Juice of fresh coconut: Cleans blood; drives away fever; cures gall-bladder and liver troubles. Drunk with lemon juice, best remedy against thirst. Mixed with dust of bitumen, it is good against pathological hiccup. Don't drink it on empty stomach (lots of it drunk on empty stomach causes dyspepsia). Drunk after meals it cures many diseases and is very beneficial for the body.

h. Hot (boiled) water: Never drink unboiled water. It contains many germs and causes many diseases. Boil it, cool it off, and then drink. There is an old saying, 'Forget butter, increase intake of butter-milk, spit out water, and Yama (= Death) won't approach you.' If you drink water before meals, it will drive away hunger. It is good to drink water after meals. If you drink much water between or with meals, diarrhoea follows. The best way to drink water is to boil it in a copper vessel and let it cool off in an iron container. Good for blood and arteries.

2. Milk

a. Female milk. A pinch of ground black pepper mixed with mother's milk produces the pungent eye-salve used as stimulant to revive an unconscious person, or to cure chronic headache. A drop into the eyes helps reduce fever within an hour.

b. Cow's milk. After the milk of female breasts, the best milk is cow's milk; equally beneficial for children and very old people. Given to sick people boiled and diluted with warm water will help healing process. Very good for pregnant women. According to ancient scriptures, it should be drunk within three hours after milking the cow. It is the source of yoghurt which is a most beneficial food.

c. Buffalo-milk. Not suitable for children (may cause diarrhoea). Should not be combined with any medicine, as it diminishes its efficacy. Not good as a source of yoghurt or butter, but very good as source of buttermilk.

d. Goat's milk. Beneficial. Good against phlegm. Taken in the morning and evening mixed with ground root and plant of Phyllanthus niruri, P. polyphyllus will cure jaundice within five days (one should of course keep on diet).

e. Sheep's milk. Not beneficial.

f. Donkey's milk. Restorative for children. Two teaspoons given for three days beginning with first day after birth will cure unhealthy colour of new infant. Excellent medicine against hysteria. Given on an empty stomach morning and evening mixed with ashes of burned tortoise-shell: it is a good restorative.

g. Coconut milk. Increases amount and quality of male semen. Excellent when warmed up with some butter as cure for stomach ulcers. May be used to tend fresh wounds.

h. Milky juice of banyan. Soothes wounds in mouth. Increases amount and quality of sperm.

i. Milky juice of figs. Drunk every morning on empty stomach after it had been placed in earthen pot to ferment: excellent remedy for leucorrhea, blood in urine and diabetes.

j. Juice of milk-hedge. Very efficient to treat wounds and tender painful spots on the body: Mix with oil and massage gently the painful spots. Boiled with juice of roots of medicinal herbs is used in treating a number of diseases.

The subchapter on milk mentions further medicinal properties of several plants like Calotropis gigantea, 'devil fig', etc.

3. Oils

a. Castor-plant oil. For children: till aged one year daily, later frequent small doses prevent diseases resulting in violent diarrhoea and fevers. Generally prevents indigestion and bowel disorders. Helps increase quantity and quality of sperm. Prescribed in some cases of bowel-hernia.

b. Rape seed (sesamum) oi!. There is a folk-saying: 'Instead of giving to the doctor, give to the oil-monger.' Oil bath once a week (of entire body) results in cooling, invigorating and beautifying the body. Used against bite of small reptiles: taken with ground black pepper it neutralizes the venom. Used also against dog-bite. Good to take when on saltless diet. Is also used in prescriptions in midwifery.

c. Oil of margosa (Azadirachta indica). Has healing properties when applied to wounds and eczemas. Used in scurf of children.

d. Oil of wild olive seeds (Bassia longifolia). Used in rheumatism and gout to apply to painful limbs. Excellent for cleaning and strengthening nails. Also used in all cases of sores, ulcers, scab and scurf.

e. Domba oil, extracted from mastwood seeds (Calophyllum inophyllum). Excellent in all cases of rheumatism and gout. Also applied for wounds, sores and scurf. In cases of severe scurf on skull or limbs, mix the oil with the kernel of mastwood fruit which had been fried almost to being scorched black and pulverized; apply repeatedly.

f. Oil extracted from seeds of Indian beech (Pongamia glabra). This oil, too, is used in wounds, sores, ulcers.

g. Coconut oil. This oil, too, is used in wounds, sores, ulcers, scab.

h. Mustard-seed oil. Excellent results when applied to rheumatic, arthritic limbs and against gout. Reduces swellings.

i. Oil extracted from marking-nuts (Semecarpus anacardium). This oil must be used with great care! Used in cases of leprosy. Also in cases of severe itching scurf and scabbiness.

j. Three in one oil. Mixture in equal proportions of rape-seed oil, castor-plant oil and cow's butter should be rubbed on one's head in cases of fever; followed by warm bath, diminishes fever and helps restore health in general.

k. Five in one oil. Castor-plant oil, rape-seed oil, margosa oil, domba oil and Pongamia glabra oil mixed in equal proportions is powerful remedy against convulsions caused by high fever. One may in addition rub 10 drops into the crown of the head. Take one teaspoon-full internally in cases of palsy and neuralgias.

4. Cowdung and other similar products

a. Cowdung. There are five products of the cow (in Sanskrit, *pancagavya*) which are considered beneficial and purifying: milk, curds, butter, urine, dung. A mixture of these five products is prescribed as a kind of 'antibiotic' against inflammatory processes. It is supposed (with some justification, to be sure) to kill germs, and that is why Hindu women clean the floor of their houses, including kitchens, with a mixture of cowdung and cow's urine.

b. Buffalo-dung. When haematemesis (vomiting blood) appears, mix one teaspoon-full of dried crushed buffalo dung in curds or buttermilk of buffalo to stop the vomiting. It also helps against jaundice.

c. Donkey-dung. Dissolve one teaspoon-full of dried crushed dung of donkey in 5 drops of buffalo buttermilk and take every morning and evening against jaundice.

d. Dung of hare. Three droppings of dung of hare taken for three successive days in the morning with a little cow-milk freshly obtained stops pregnancy. Taken in excess can cause barrenness.

5. Urine

a. Human urine (Tam: *cirunir*). There is one Siddha school which prescribes administration of one dosis (1 tablespoon-full) of the urine of a female child to a male child, and of the urine of a male child to a female child next day after they are born as remedy against erysipelas on head of children. The urine must be of children who are not older than age 5. Other than that, human urine is used in the 'science of longevity' (see below), and sometimes in the sexual sphere (see below).

b. Cow's urine. Very effective against internal parasites, jaundice (both acute, infectious, and chronic) and dropsy. On prescription and administration obtained only from Siddha physicians. Goat-urine can be used instead.

c. Horse-urine. Used as remedy against scrofous eruption on feet. If applied to infected wounds soaked in a piece of cotton it will kill germs and has healing properties.

d. Donkey-urine. A dosis of teaspoon-full twice daily morning and evening is a remedy against a number of afflictions and diseases: loss of semen, sexually transmitted diseases, leprosy, asthma and consumption.

6. Sugars

a. Juice of sugar-cane. If eaten in moderation, will affect beneficially bilious temper. Used to refine brimstone which is used when one suffers from aversion to food and vomiting. It is also employed when preparing important life-prolonging medicine.

b. Cane-sugar (only in coarse form, as jaggery prepared from cane-molasses). Moderate intake is used as antidote in excess of bile. Will help in getting rid of phlegm.

c. Coarse sugar from palmyra-juice. As jaggery, it will strengthen the body. Used as antidote against bilious disorders and aversion to food. Decoction of jaggery with dry ginger will give relief in muscle-pain; also, general pain-killer.

d. White refined sugar. Moderate intake helps against excess of bile. Mixture of butter and sugar will stop hiccup. In excess may cause diabetes.

e. Candied sugar. The best of all sugars. Strengthens the body, stops bilious afflictions.

f. Candied palmyra-sugar. Very good remedy against fever.

g. Candied honey-sugar. A mixture of so-called *tirikatuku* i.e. the three stimulants of dry ginger, black pepper and long pepper powder mixed with honey-sugar will strengthen the voice; a must for all singers.

7. Intoxicants

The attitude of Siddha medicine vis-à-vis alcoholic beverages is generally negative (apart from Tantrik Siddhas and their intake of liquor during Tantrik rites). The texts mention only *kal*, *kallu*, i.e. fermented sap or toddy, of three kinds: made from coconut palm, from palmyra palm (Borassus flabelliformis) and from sandal tree (Santalum album). The negative effects of the first variety are mentioned with warning; the second variety is admitted to have some positive effects, too: it invigorates the body generally, and increases amount of male sperm. The third variety is said to 'cool off' the body and to give relief when there is 'obstruction of urine'. [4]

8. Honey

Interestingly enough, Siddha medicine, while enthusiastically recommending honey as remedy against a number of ailments, also warns against excessive use of it. Twice a day, morning and evening, one may eat just one teaspoon-full. Very beneficial (especially for the throat, and for improving the quality of voice) is mixture of milk and honey.[5] In general, honey is supposed to generate keen appetite, loosen phlegm, be excellent remedy in cases of consumption, and help against hiccup. Most importantly: mixture of honey and lemon juice in the ratio 1:3 is excellent for slimming.

9. Trees

As may be expected, most items in Siddha materia medica come from the various trees, bushes, creepers, plants and grasses, roots and tubers, more or less readily available in South India.

---

4 Siddha medicine does not know grape-wine.

5 This mixture appears very early in Tamil classical poetry, and becomes, in Tamil culture, symbolic of health, prosperity and beauty. The famous *Tirukkural* (4th or 5th century A.D.) has this distich (113. 1): 'The juice that oozes from the white teeth of the soft-speeched girl / is like a mixture of milk and honey.'

a. Sandal (Santalum album). Ground and mixed with water into paste, sandal-wood is used generally in India in cosmetics; also as incense. Specifically, against female leucorrhoea: grind sandal wood on a stone, mix with water, take 2-3 drops twice a day. Is equally beneficial in cases of gonorrhoea. Increases and cleans male sperm.

b. Deodar (a kind of cedar). Its dust mixed with oil and heated should be rubbed on the forehead against headache, and is very helpful when rubbed on and around the nose when one has a cold.

c. Neem (Melia azadirachta). This tree, known also as margosa, is of immense value in Siddha medicine, and the outstanding anti-inflammatory and anti-arthritic properties of its oil have been tested by modern methods. Decoction prepared from its bark is considered general tonic and life-prolonging agent. Neem oil contains sodium nimbidinate, nimbidol, nimbin and nimbinin. It was found in tests performed in Pharmacology Laboratory of Indian Institute of Science (Bangalore) that neem oil is nearly as effective as cortisone and sodium salicylate in checking the extent of development of oedema after formaldehyde injection. The experiments have shown that neem oil and its bitter components possess varying degrees of anti-inflammatory properties. Nimbidol exhibited powerful inhibitory effect on formaline-induced arthritis. On the whole, fair degree of relief from pain and considerable reduction of the swelling of joints and tissues were definitely observed in cases of rheumatoid arthritis.[6] The leaves of margosa smeared with turmeric give relief to fresh small-pox wounds. Decoction prepared from ground bark is said to have good effects in cases of diabetes.

d. Indian horse-radish tree (Moringa pterygosperma). Its ground bark, mixed with mustard seed (Brassica juncea) and garlic, and made into a thick sauce will, eaten with rice, cure rheumatic afflictions. Its blossoms, boiled in fresh milk, will be eaten to thicken male sperm. Another recipe for improving and thickening semen: Eat often boiled rice with curry

---

6 Experiments performed on rats' paws with arthritis induced by formaldehyde (resulting in acute hyperaemia and oedema of rheumatic type, and chronic reactions of rheumatoid type) were described by Dr. David S. Narayan. Cf. also Narayananan, David Shankara, 'Antiarthritic and Anti-inflammatory Activity of Neem Oil (*Melia azadirachta linn*) and its Constituents', *Proceedings, Second International Conference Seminar of Tamil Studies*, Madras, January 1968, publ. 1971, Vol. Two, 545-52.

prepared from its leaves with ground sesame seeds. This is also used against diabetes. Its resin is also said to thicken semen.

Other trees used in Siddha medicine are pipal (Ficus religiosa), babul (Acacia arabica = Mimosa arabica) whose resin is used to make sperm thick and healthy as well as a drug against diabetes, Prosopia spicigera, a prickly tree with an eatable pod, etc.

10. Bushes and plants

Innumerable bushes and plants yield in their leaves, blossoms, fruits, bark and roots substances used in Siddha pharmacopoeia. The text in question gives a list of 48 medicinal plants. These comprise tanner's senna (Cassia articulata), Diospyros tomentosa, Abubilon asiaticum (indicum, Indian mallow or country mallow), datura (different varieties), Barleria longifolia etc. One of the most widely used plants is tulaci (tulsi, Ocimum sanctum), sacred basil which has powerful healing properties: it is used against all kinds of cold (fever, cough, phlegm, running nose, catarrhs), in particular in children (its juice mixed with honey). Barleria is employed as diureticum. Datura, which is poisonous, has some very special uses: three drops of the juice of its leaves in a cup of milk are used in the cure of mental disorders, but its leaves are also applied to wounds originated from dogs' bites. Patchouli (Indian marjoram, Pogostemon spp.) is used in cases of malaria and other fevers. Sesamum orientale (black sesame, gingelly plant) gives oil which is of course used in cuisine, but has also rich application in Siddha medicine.

11. Creepers and plants

Equally rich and variegated is the subchapter on creepers and plants. The source in question quotes 33 species. The ones most important and most widely used seem to be the following: Vitis quadrangularis, a shrub called pirandei or purandei in Tamil (square-stalked vine), used against (bleeding) piles and haemorrhoids; experiments have shown that after repeated cure (powdered dried stalks eaten mornings and evenings for a week), operation was not necessary. It is also used, mixed with honey, in chronic dyspepsia, and to improve general health.

Panicum verticillatum (its Tamil name meaning, literally, 'horse-tail') is used against ulcers, pain from piles and yet other diseases but also, its juice mixed with coconut oil, rubbed daily into one's hair, is an important hair tonic.

Bryonia Mysorensis: used against ulceration in the head running off through nostrils and cold affecting the nose.

Other creepers and plants used in Siddha medicine: Verbena nodiflora, Caparis horrida, Coleus aromaticus (a camphor- smelling plant, the juice of its leaves being used against collection of phlegm in infants), Eclipta alba, employed in the rejuvenation process (this plant being so-called *kayasiddhi*, i.e. having the power of securing the body against the effects of age), etc.

One of the most potent herbs seems to be a thorny thistle called 'cow's thorn', Tribulus terrestris. It is used in the following cases: in strangury (stoppage or suppression of urine) and retention of urine by gravel; it purifies blood and increases the count of red blood corpuscules; it removes swelling in feet, hands, and is used as general diureticum. Modern experiments have proven its efficacy.

12. Grasses

Seven kinds of 'grasses' (*pul, pullu*) are named as useful in medicine:

1. Yellow-flowered aloe (Aloe typica), known also from other medical systems, and said to be very potent: it helps against blood in urine and in faeces, against haemorrhoids, stomach disorders, fever etc. One tablespoon-full taken twice daily of its juice mixed with ten measures of cold water, palmyra candied sugar and dry cumin (Cuminum cyminum) helps in above-mentioned disorders and can be applied externally to haemorrhoids, too.

2. Red-flowered aloe.

3. Cynodon dactylon seems to be equally efficacious. It is used as antidote against poisons, in particular snake-venoms. Everyone is recommended to drink at least once a month a decoction prepared from this grass mixed with black pepper; it cures many diseases, and is specifically good against 'heart-burn'. Other medicinal grasses: cintronella grass (used against infantile diarrhoea and indigestion), etc. A mushroom, Agaricus campestris (Tamil: *kalan*) is classified under this heading.

13. Parts of trees, mainly roots

Most frequently employed tree-roots and tree-bark are those of pipal (Ficus religiosa), vilvam (Crataeva religiosa), banyan (Ficus bengalensis), Indian mulberry, citron lemon and jujub. Portia tree (Thespia) is apparently also very potent: its buds and young leaves are used against jaundice; the bark of old portia trees is used even in cases of leprosy (!) etc. The twigs of banyan are generally used all over India as toothbrush; at the same time, the juice oozing from chewed twigs is said to help in cases of stomach ulcers. The ground seed of banyan mixed with pipal seed and fig seed as well as with red iron-oxide, all this administered in honey, is believed to strengthen the body in general, and make male semen more potent in particular. The leaves of Zizyphus jujuba are used against haemorrhoids. Another tree with manifold employ is Morinda citrifolia alias Indian mulberry: it is said to be most effective as decoction from its leaves given to children against diarrhoea and other bowel disorders; its fruits, roots and bark are also used. Citrus medica (citron lemon): its fruit has antiseptic properties and should be eaten to generally strengthen the body; its flowers and buds, ground and mixed in buttermilk, help in cases of diarrhoea and dysentery.

14. Tubers and roots

As can be expected, roots and tubers of many varieties are used in Siddha medicine. The basic sources quote at least 90 (!) different kinds of roots / tubers. Some of those most frequently and effectively employed are mentioned below. In Siddha pharmacopoeia, distinction is made between 'tubers' and 'roots'.

14. 1. Tubers (kizhangu).

a. Turmeric (Curcuma longa) has very wide range of use: it removes (so it is maintained) the stench of raw meat or fish from the body's perspiration; more importantly, it is used against headache, cold, sores and ulcers, pulmonary infections, and all kinds of disorders caused by phlegm. In addition, it is employed in erotic charms to attract men.

b. Radish (Raphanus sativus) is considered extremely healthy. It is used as remedy in cases of consumption, scurf, chronic dyspepsia, gout, painful piles and flatulency.

c. Ginger: fresh ginger is used in cardiology, and to stop nausea and vomiting, diarrhoea and dysentery.

d. Lotus root is used in ophtalmology.

e. Onion is regarded, too, as having healing properties. It is used as a remedy in cases of sexually transmitted diseases, haemorrhoids, fevers, but is warned against being used in excess.

f. Young edible palmyra root (Borassus flabelliformis) is used against too much bodily 'heat', and is employed in cosmetics, but may cause itch and eruptions.

g. Citrullus colocynthis: its tubers are very effective purgative, used with success in cases of chronic constipation (experimentally verified by Western medicine).

h. Goa potato (Dioscorea aculeata). This should **not** be eaten. Believed to cause or adversely influence various diseases, such as itching rash, development of piles, flatulency etc. The same is true about other kinds of Dioscorea (bulbifera Malacca yam, betel yam, humped yam etc.).

14. 2. Roots.

When one studies the list of roots (*veer*) which are used in Siddha pharmacopoeia one cannot escape the impression that roots of almost any tree or bush are responsible for some effects on human body-mind, beneficial or adverse. The most frequently employed roots are:

a. mango root: immediate remedy against dysentery (including bloody slime in excreta) and vomiting.

b. root of trumpet-flower tree (Stereospermum chelonoides, suaveolens and xylocarpum): remedy against burning sensations and piles.

c. root of Michelia champaka: causes keen appetite; diminishes 'heat' in body.

d. root of Indian beech (Pongamia glabra): the juice pressed out of the root at once heals all internal wounds and ulcers.

e. root of jamoon plum (Eugenia jambolana): used as effective remedy in cases of bloody diarrhoea, flatulency, ulcers, diabetes.

f. root of country fig (Ficus glomerata): the ground upper crust of its root is used against leucorrhoea ('the whites'); fermented juice of the root is used in various sexually transmitted diseases.

g. root of emblic myrobalan (Phyllanthus emblica): the ground upper crust of the root cures cases of aversion for food and chronic dyspepsia, and is used against vomiting and indigestion.

h. finally, the root of strychnine tree (Strychnos nux vomica). This is a very potent factor in the cure of big-snake bites, and is used in Siddha psychiatry. There is a specific prescription against what is designated as 'confusion' or 'distraction' of mind: dissolve 3 grams of finely ground root in 4 cups of cold water; reduce by boiling to 1 cup, add red ochre soil, cauterized (burned with a caustic substance), and administer in the morning on empty stomach; this remedy is also prescribed in cases of disorders caused by saltless diet (followed by food containing high amount of iron). Given also in cases of psychoses, twice a week.

After this somewhat bizarre passage one must add that the textual sources quote under this heading the use of five all-important mixtures of roots / tubers, which have been current in South India for some 2000 years:

1. 'Fivefold root' (*pancamulam*) is a mixture of powdered long pepper (Piper longum), dry ginger, root of Ceylon leadwort (Plumbago zeylanica), beetle-killer and big galangal (Alpinia galanga). Used as powder or electuary (powder mixed with honey) it cures many diseases.

2. 'Little fivefold root' (*sirupancamulam*) is a mixture of powdered root of Indigofera enneaphylla, wild jasmine (Jasminum augustifolium), Indian nightshade (Solanum indicum), Solanum xanthocarpum and Arabian jasmine (Jasminum sambac - heyneana). Used as powder or electuary.

3. 'Large fivefold root' (*perupancamulam*): mixture of powdered roots of trumpet-flower tree (Stereospermum), coomb teak (Gmelia arborea), bael (vilva), sirissa (Albizzia) and wind-killer (Aegle marmelos): carminative medicine.

4. 'Eightfold root' (*astamulam*): mixture of powdered root of the grass Cyperus rotundus, the creeper Tinospora cordifolia (gulansh), medicinal herb Ocimum album, malabar nut, black basil (Ocimum sanctum typica), medicinal plant Pharnaceum cerviana, Indian globe-thistle and wild snake-gourd (Trichosanthes cucumerina).

5. 'Tenfold root' (*tasamulam*): mixture of powdered root of Aegle marmelos (vilva), Jasminum augustifolium, Jasminum sambac, Stereospermum, Indigofera enneaphylla, Solanum indicum, Gmelia arborea, Albizzia lebbek (sirissa), firebrand teak (Premna integrifolia) and Pedalium murex (a stout-stemmed herb with spiny fruits and slimy leaves).

15. Spices and other commodities, available commercially

a. Dry ginger is an omnipotent drug. In particular, in combination with common and long pepper it is regarded as the best organic drug available. This combination of Zingiberos (dry ginger), Piper longum (long pepper) and Piper nigrum (black pepper) known since ancient times as *Tirikatukam* ('Threefold pungency')[7] is also employed as important component of drugs used in methods of rejuvenation and for supporting longevity. Specifically, dry ginger is used against headache, indigestion, palpitation of the heart, diarrhoea, phlegm, asthma, bleeding piles, and all kinds of stiffness of the limbs caused by arthritis and rheumatism.

b. Black pepper (Piper nigrum) is used as component of many drugs. The same is true of long pepper (Piper longum).

c. Indian gall-nut (ink-nut, chebulic myrobalan, Terminalia chebula). Excellent against piles. Administered in buttermilk excellent against diarrhoea.

d. Cardamom (Elettaria cardamomum; various sorts) is very often employed as drug in the following cases: headache, cough, phlegm and mucus, diarrhoea and dysentery, vomiting.

e. Cumin (Cuminum cyminum): effective against stomach-aches, cold affecting nose, etc. Also used as digestive and in cases of aversion to food.

f. Coriander (Coriandrum sativum): excellent for increase of sperm; used against vomiting, pathological hiccup, dryness of the tongue.

g. Asafoetida (Ferula). Used, dissolved as powder in water, against bites by scorpions. Increases digestion. Employed against abscesses, boils and tumours in the vagina (rubbed deep into its inner walls). Used against flatulence in digestive tract.[8]

h. Garlic. Effective in cases of dropsy, headache caused by hypertension, convulsions and apoplexy, rheumatism and gout.

i. Camphor is used as remedy in cases of dropsical swellings, worms in intestines, colic and stomachaches, but also in otholaryngology.

j. Musk (kastoori, secretion from the navel of musk-deer): cures common cold, running nose, fever caused by cold. Given during

---

7 In fact, a small collection of didactic maxims in four-line stanzas by Nallatanar, entitled *Tirikatukam* (Three pungent spices) dates from about A. D. 725. As a support for achieving longevity and perfect health even in advanced age one should eat this mixture of powders every morning mixed in a teaspoon-full of honey. Experimentally documented in geriatrics.

8 Asafoetida, asafetida (Indian name: *hing*), somewhat smelly brown resin used mainly for its digestive properties and its truffle-like flavour and fragrance. It is available both in lump form and as grainy powder. The lump is supposed to be purer. Mild purgative.

parturition in pure form (very small quantity of ca. a grain of rice) on betel-leaf it will stop convulsions.

k. Mustard-seed (different kinds). Used in obstetrics as decoction; against venomous bites of large reptiles; in cases of bites by insects and bee-sting. Mustard ointment is to be employed against large swellings.

16. Salts

An odd assortment of substances apart from certain true salts is quoted under the heading of 'salts' (*uppu*): verdigris, green vitriol, amber, frankincense, resin, mica, rock alum, asbestos, red chalk, Meerschaum, bismuth, shell of pearl oyster, etc. etc. Some of these substances may be innocent enough and have been experimentally tested in contemporary Siddha medicine with healing effects. Thus kitchen salt is used against indigestion and aversion to food. Sulphur-salt is employed against severe diarrhoea and flatulence.[9] A very special medicine is prepared so that a fowl is stuffed with bdellium (kind of resin) and then calcinated: this is supposed to improve general health in old people (hence used in the attempts at longevity) and also have healing properties in cases of chronic diarrhoea, rheumatism in the joints, sores and ulcers. Bismuth is supposed to increase the quantity of male semen. Even odder are the following items: ashes from burnt peacock-feathers (used against hiccup) ; indragopa insect (Coccus cacti, cochineal insect of red colour) used in cases of nocturnal pollution, and generally in *kayacitti*;[10] eggs laid by large red ants (used against spasms, convulsions and convulsive fits), earthworms, etc. Visions of witches' cauldrons arise before our eyes.

17. 'Stones' (i.e. minerals, mineral drugs and poisons)

These substances are widely used in Siddha pharmacopoeia, although their use is not without danger.

---

9 A case was reported in *The European* (Elan 17, 14. -20. 1. 94) of a Dutch woman (Geraldine Vink) suffering from a grave case of multiple sclerosis (MS) whose health substantially improved after homoeopathic therapy with a highly dilute mixture of sulphure and carbonate of lime - a drug corresponding exactly to some prescriptions of Tamil Siddha practitioners.

10 *Kayacitti* (kaayasiddhi) is the specific term for the power of securing the body against the effects of old age.

a. Mercury (called in Siddha paribhasha *civaviriyam* or *civavintu* or, *sivabija* i.e. 'Siva's seed') is, as its Siddha name implies, regarded as an all-powerful substance. However, the use of quicksilver in therapy (even according to the Siddhas) is loaded with danger. If, however, it is employed with caution and experience and, above all, according to secret prescriptions handed down orally, it is beneficial in treatment of several grave diseases.

b. Vermillion (red sulphurate, hydrargyri bisulphuretum). This substance is made out of a combination of mercury and brimstone, and is used as part of a number of medicines.

c. Cavviram is a strong medicinal compound containing quicksilver, ammonia, alum, etc., sublimated. It is potent poison, used in therapy in cases of chronic dyspepsia, rheumatism, arthritis, flatulency, bloated body, etc.

d. Aritaram, yellow sulphuret of arsenic, found in nature, is used in cases of consumption and the resulting fevers, syphilitic ulcer (called 'Frankish wound'), leprosy, etc.

e. Orpiment (auripigment), very difficult to obtain.

f. Plumbi oxidum (impure oxide of lead; adopted from North India, cf. its Urdu name murdarsingh); found in nature. Used in treatment of dangerous ulcers and sores, large wounds, chronic scab, sexually transmitted diseases, in short, mostly in dermatology and treatment of sexually transmitted diseases. Dangerous.

g. Sublimate of mercury is a natural substance, difficult to find. Supposed to be very effective in malaria, elephantiasis and filaria.

All in all, Siddha texts quote 32 mineral drugs / poisons. Typical for these substances are three features: they are all employed in cases of grave / terminal / 'incurable' diseases; second, textual sources never give exact prescriptions how to use them in therapy; third, contemporary Siddha physicians are reluctant to discuss them. The actual prescriptions are in almost all cases handed down orally from generation to generation (*parampara*).

18. Metals

There is a great variety in the usage of metals in Siddha pharmacopoeia. Most Siddha sources quote eight metals: gold, silver, copper, tin, lead, iron, steel and zinc. There are, however, other lists available. I was able to come up with a list of 13 metals/metal combinations.

1. Gold. As medicinal powder, gold improves the quality of sperm. It is used in treatment of consumption and rheumatism.

2. Silver is very frequently employed in treatment of sexually transmitted diseases, rheumatism, the whites, to purge blood, in obstruction of chest or throat by thick phlegm, etc.

3. Copper is even more potent; it is used in treatment of all diseases mentioned above, plus dropsy of the belly, sores and ulcers, nocturnal emission, white leprosy and bilious fever.

4. Brass increases sperm-count. It has 'cooling' effect, and is a remedy against rheumatic afflictions.

5. Bell-metal increases, too, sperm-count. It is used in cases of dropsy of the belly, rheumatism, arthritis, gout.

6. Mixture of copper and spelter: copper made black by melting spelter or zinc with it. This is effective against arthritis, rheumatic fever and leucorrhoea.

7. Tin, pewter. Employed against high fever, scurf and cutaneous eruptions, sexually transmitted disease.

8. Lead. Used in treatment of leprosy, sexually transmitted diseases, sores and ulcers.

9. Zinc. Brings about great appetite. Used in cases of chronic diarrhoea, the whites, etc.

10. Iron. Very beneficial in general. Used in cases of overall bodily weakness, and in treatment of jaundice, stomach diseases, dyspepsia, aversion to food, impotence, nocturnal pollution. Increases count of sperm, induces healthy state of semen. Promotes longevity. In excess, produces diarrhoea.

11. Steel. Used effectively in cases of unhealthy semen. Promotes copious sperm. Effective against swellings and in cases of weakness and infirmity.

12. Load-stone, magnet: promotion of longevity; against swellings, jaundice, frigidity, aversion to food, in ophthalmology.

13. Oxide of iron, iron-dross: promotes healthy state of blood; used in cases of severe poisoning; against swellings, etc.

19. Nine gems

The 'nine gems' (*navaratna*) used in some branches of Siddha medical practice are ruby, diamond, beryl, onyx, topaz, coral, pearl, emerald and sapphire. Most of these are indigenous to India. Obviously, contemporary practice does not make much use of these materials because of their high price. Traditionally, though, some of the 'gems' were used in cases of, e.g., 'flatulency inducing melancholy and hypochondria' (beryl, onyx), collection of phlegm (beryl, coral), unhealthy state of male semen (sapphire, coral), sexually transmitted diseases (topaz) etc. Diamond was supposed to enhance physical beauty, coral to foster body's lustre, onyx to cause the body shine with health, etc.

20. Male semen, etc.

Some Siddha texts add three discharges of the body (and their mixture) connected with male and female sexual functions to the list of effective 'drugs'.

a. Semen (sperm). Various terms are used, either in plain Tamil, or in the 'twilight language' (specific professional jargon) of the Siddhas to denote this stuff: (*cukkilam*) (< Skt. 'whiteness, white substance'; (*intiriyam*) (< Skt.), lit. 'virile power', i.e. that which is fit for or belonging to god Indra, the lord of the gods of the sky; (*viriyam*) lit. 'vigour; power'; (*velli*) lit. 'whiteness; silver'; (*vintu*; *pintu*) lit. 'drop; dot over a letter; spot, mark'. It should be white, thick, fragrant and copious; thick consistency of semen (termed *viriyakkattu*) is much sought after. Prescribed as beneficial when taken by women while still fresh during or immediately after coition. Sperm, when swallowed mixed with ground pepper, is considered to be of great rejuvenating power fit for both men and women, provided it is 'healthy'.

b. 'Female semen' (*semen muliebre*), termed usually *natam*; (however, this term is used also to refer to germ cell, ovum, ovule gerum) or *conitam* (lit. 'red, crimson; blood', referring also to menstrual blood), or, in the professional metaphoric jargon, *curatanir*, lit. 'juice of sexual union', or, *kamanir,* lit. 'juice of lust', or even, *kamappal*, lit. 'milk of lust', or simply, *tiravam* lit. 'liquid, juice' (these terms refer also sometimes to prostatic secretion in sexually aroused males). 'Female semen' should be sucked by men before or during coitus.

c. Menstrual discharge (*conitam*, *irattam*, *rajas*) is considered impure and very dangerous in general. However, there are other opinions among the Siddhas which not only allow but, so it would seem, recommend coitus during the time of the woman's monthly periods. Menstrual blood is believed to be 'in the womb causing pregnancy when mixed with semen' (*Tamil Lexicon* 1533).[11]

d. The mixture of male sperm and female sex-discharge, termed *cukkilaconitam* is supposed to be (according to some Siddha sources) especially beneficial: invigorating, lust-increasing, it should be licked and swallowed by men immediately after coitus, 'fresh' from the labia of the vulva.

However, one must warn the readers that these recommendations pertain only to one (minor!) section of Siddha practitioners and stem only from one lineage of Siddha tradition. There is an opposite tendency present in contemporary Siddha tradition, too. Thus, e. g., Vi. Palaramayya in one of his publications (1975) in Tamil on the daily regime of Siddha practitioner says: 'We engage in sex with women once a week. A person who will spend semen uselessly will not get ill but his thinking abilities and his memory will be negatively affected' .

The recommendations concerning ingestion of sperm, female discharge and the mixture of the two are connected with the notions about the origin of life. Since there has almost never been any taboo attached to dealing with and discussion of sexual matters, the Siddha tradition, in agreement with general Hindu attitudes, includes also recommendations of this type in the attempt to foster vitality and induce processes of rejuvenation and longevity.[12]

Diseases and their cure with prescriptions

Introducing this part of the work, I wish to cite the nine texts in Tamil, all belonging to the Siddha Tamil tradition, on which it is based: *Cittararutaccintu*, a work on toxicology (published in 1916 by Gurusami Konar); *Akattiyar purana cuttiram*, on methods of preparing rare medicines; *Akattiyarcuvami kaviya nikantu*, versified dictionary of healing and medicine in 8 chapters; *Akatticar vakatam*, 1500 stanzas on

---

[11] Cf. *Cilappatikaram 3. 26, commentary* which reads, 'life originates . . . with the body [after mixture] of sperm and menstrual discharge (or, female semen).' (U. V. Swaminatha Iyer's ed., Madras, 1950, p. 104).

[12] Cf. also Padmanabhan, N., 'Hypotensive Effects of Carica Papaya', *Proceedings, Second International Conference Seminar of Tamil Studies*, publ. 1971, Vol. Two, 553-55; Uthamaroyan, C. S., 'Treatment of (Chronic Arthritis) Joint Disease', *ibid.* 535-40 ; Shanmugavelu, M., 'Mercury - the Universal Remedy "for almost all Diseases" according to Siddhas' Concept', *ibid.*, 531-34.

medicine in general; *Iramatevar Civayokam*: work which synchronizes worship of many different deities with medical practices and preparations of drugs, in verse; *Tanvantiri vaittiyam* alias *Yukimuni castiram* supposed to have been revealed by Siva to Uma, by Uma to Nandi, by Nandi to the Siddhas Tanvantiri, Acuvinitevar and Akattiyamuni; *Potikai munnuru*, 301 stanzas by Potikaiyar (i.e. Akastiyar); *Vaittiyakaviyam* alias *Akastiyar vakatam*, in 493 stanzas; *Patarttakunam* ('Qualities of Drugs') in 11 stanzas. In addition, there was of course information gathered from contemporary Siddha practitioners. [13] The following pages contain a typical selection of Siddha attitudes vis-à-vis certain diseases, and examples of Siddha therapy: peptic ulcer, arthritis, haemorrhoids, skin diseases, dental care and problems, surgery, poisons.

1. Peptic ulcer

Yukimuni's *Vaittiya cintamani perunul 800* describes the aetiology of peptic ulcer in admirably precise terms. Ulcer (*kunmam*) is the result of 1. excessive consumption of astringent (*tuvar*) food, or 2. excessive indulgence in sexual intercourse, or 3. excessive consumption of roots and sharp spices, or 4. irregular food habits, or 5. negative emotions (anger, anxiety). As a result, *pittam* (bile) responsible for secretion of gastric juices, becomes 'deranged', increased secretion induces *tapitam*, inflammation of the mucous membranes of the stomach and duodenum, and this results in *kukkippun*, i.e. peptic ulcer. The remedy generally used in Siddha therapy is *tampira centuram*, the astringent, sedative, antispasmodic, antiseptic, emetic and purgative drug prepared from copper, lime juice and juice of Ocymum sanctum (sacred basil). It is however necessary to follow scrupulously the mode of its preparation:[14] 100 g of copper filings soaked in lime juice for 5 days. Old juice is removed daily, the filings are cleaned with fresh water, then soaked in fresh juice. On 6th day, they are dried in the sun. Subsequently, they are ground finely with the juice of Ocymum sanctum (*karuntulaci*, sacred basil). Made into small pills, they are dried in the sun, placed in mud pans and sealed with 7 mud plasters. These are subjected to the process of purification by heat using about a hundred cowdung cakes. After

13 A seminar on Siddha medicine was held at the International Institute of Tamil Studies, Madras, on 21. 3. 1984 - 23. 3. 1984.

14 According to Dr. M. Sundaram and Dr. G. Veluchamy of Central Research Institute for Siddha, Madras.

cooling down, the pills are taken out, and the whole process is repeated for 7 days; finally they are powdered. The colour of the powder will be slightly reddish-black. This drug was used first on rats and guinea pigs, then on patients who were examined by X-rays etc., and found to suffer from peptic ulcers. They were given the drug in capsules of 43 mg, 1 capsule twice daily before meals. The entire treatment ran in 3 courses of 5 days each, alternating with 2 days of rest. Patients were advised to keep to a diet (mostly boiled rice gruel, white bread, butter, milk; no meat, no spices). Most cases showed significant improvement: some were discharged with a complete cure, many with the disappearance of clinical symptoms. It was also found out that the drug was effective in post-operative treatment. Thus it seems that the drug can be considered effective in treatment for peptic ulcer if devoid of perforations and haemorrhage. It has no side effects or toxic reactions with the dose as mentioned above, and is available at low cost.

2. Arthritis (kilvayu)

The Tamil term includes all kinds of joint disorders; it is classified into 5, 6, 10 or 25 varieties, and as the main causes of arthritic disorders are described errors of diet, exposure to severe cold, cold rain, fog, extensive intake of cold substances, excessive sexual indulgence, or hereditary causes. Symptoms are described in great detail and with great accuracy. The following principles should be adopted with the treatment of arthritis:

a. Causative factors should be noted and removed (e.g. if the patient lives in a cold, damp place he has to change his / her residence);

b. Rest combined with controlled movement should be observed. Rest is of three kinds - systemic rest, emotional rest and articulatory rest;

c. Purgatives are given as first measure, as in all treatment of rheumatic (*vatam*) diseases;

d. Direct and specific remedies consist of herbal and / or anorganic preparations;

e. Other special remedies (external application, fumigation etc.) are prescribed;

f. Yogic asanas (controlled) are recommended: cobra pose, plough pose, bow pose, alternate toe-touching with side bend, sitting forward-twist. Simultaneously, both diaphragmatic and abdominal breathing exercises are prescribed (to maintain mobility of the thorax);

g. Diet: when there is fever, liquid rice-gruel should be eaten. Later boiled rice, tender egg-plant, softly boiled lentils, lady's fingers and other easily digestible food may be given. Soups prepared from goat's chest-bone and joint-bones as well as goat's heart decoction and lamb-meat may be eaten.

The inorganic preparations consist of *paspam* (metals reduced to medical powders) and *cinturam* (red chemical preparations from metals or minerals) containing lead, gold etc. These can be dangerous.[15] Externally, a number of ointments are also applied, e.g. Molucca bean leaves, seeds and peas are ground and applied; a mixture of horse-radish tree leaves, Cleome felina leaves and other leaves are gently fried in castor oil, applied to the joints and bandaged. Dried bark of very old tamarind tree is burned over a broad stone; the juice of hedge-twiner mixed with powder of black quick-lime is poured over the heated stone after removing the ash and boiled to semisolid paste which is applied still very warm to the affected joint. If the swelling is large, application of good leeches relieves the tension. Fumigation of the affected joint is also used, combined with a salt-free diet and castor oil baths.

3. Haemorrhoids (piles).

Internal, interno-external and external haemorrhoids arise in the lower regions of the rectum and some parts of the anal canal. The Siddha medicine uses many synonyms for piles (*mulanoy, atimulanoy* etc.). According to the Siddhas (e.g. *Tirumular Natinul*, p. 275), the following causes are attributed to this disease: unsuitable feeding excesses because of eating pungent, sour, salty or hot food; fasts (!); want of movement; sleep by day (the Siddhas warn repeatedly against sleep by day!); riding; squatting; sexual extravagance; suppression of excretion; grief and anger. According to Teraiyar, there are 10 types of piles (*mulam*), but other sources enumerated between 9 - 21 types (including *meka mulam*, associated with gonorrhoea; piles associated with constipation and flatulence; with prolapse, etc.). Treatment consists, first of all, in laxatives; secondarily, in fumigation, external application and ointments. Most frequently recommended laxatives: 1. Rose-petals soaked in honey. 2. Dried grapes with honey. 3. For bleeding piles and constipation: Fry tender fruits of Terminalia chebula (35 gms) in 1400 gms of castor oil; when brown, take out and powder; mix the powder with the castor oil. 1-

---

[15] Hence no detailed prescription is given here.

2 teaspoons at bed-time (see *Cittavaittiyattirattu* p. 348). 4. Mixture of Carum roxburghianum (35 gms), Zingiber officinale (35 gms), root of Plumbago rosea (35 gms) and Terminalia chebula (105 gms), purified and powdered. 3-4 grams thrice daily in buttermilk. All types of piles. 5. Brassica nigra (mustard-seed, 35 gms), Sesamum indicum (35 gms), Piper longum (35 gms), Zingiber officinale (ginger, 325 gms), purified and powdered; 1-2 gms twice daily with honey.

Among some more specific laxatives with anti-pile properties may be quoted the following: *Nakacenturam*: zinc (1400 gms), potassium nitrate (4000 gms), ginger (140 gms), Carum roxburghianum (1000 gms), Curcuma longa (turmeric, 140 gms), Achyranthes aspera (5500 gms), plus sufficient lime-juice. Melt zinc in pan. Add small quantities of potassium and curcuma, and mix until metal attains powdery form. Grind product with lime juice and other components for 5 days; make cakes, dry and calcine using 300 cow-dung cakes. Repeat grinding with lime-juice and calcination 12 to 14 more times. The result should be brown in colour. Administer 100-200 mg with the three-pungent powder (*tirikatuku*).

Other remedies consist of a. steam bath, b. vapour bath, c. fumigation and d. diet.

a. Ginger (Zingiber officinale), turmeric (Curcuma longa), pepper (Piper longum) and Carum roxburghianum are ground, heated and mixed with water; the body is covered with a sheet and exposed to its steam (cf. *Teraiyar venpa* 132).

b. Leaves of Vitex negundo (*nocci*) tree are boiled with water, hot burnt brick is inserted into the boiled water, body covered with sheet and exposed to the steam.

c. The flesh of a crocodile is heated, and the anal canal is exposed to the smoke.

d. Easily digestible food should be eaten; salty and acrid things avoided. Overeating and excessive consumption of alcohol causes portal congestion and favours formation of piles, hence should be avoided.

4. Skin diseases

The Siddha classification of skin diseases is into four groups: dermatitis, abscesses, tumours, leprosy and cancer. Dermatitis (*carumappun*) generally represents inflammatory conditions of the skin (12 types), and covers inflammations caused by contusions and laceration, heat, chills and colds, sexually transmitted ulcers, pruritus, exanthemata, acne, psoriaris etc. There are Siddha drugs and treatments available against all these conditions. I shall describe selectively some of the most common therapies.

Contusions are treated with paste or juice (applied externally) of Agave americana and Aloe indica. Acne (acute or chronic, with symptoms of small pustules, common usually in youths, on neck and back): fresh rind of lime fruit should be rubbed on the skin; paste of Veronia anthelmintica (purple fleabane) with vinegar is also good remedy (externally). A number of skin diseases is connected with genital problems: genital ulcers are termed *kiranti*, and they are of three main types: gonorrhoea (*mekavettai*), chancre and syphilis (*mekappun*) and chancroid (*kurukkuppun*). Remedies are available against all three. Example: For gonorrhoea (sometimes called incorrectly *vellai* or 'the whites'), the treatment consists of a certain paste and a drug composed as follows: fried alum, dried Emblica myrobalan and sugar candy, each to be powdered separately, mixed in equal portions, taken in doses of 1 gm with 2-3 drops of sandalwood oil with butter or milk for three days.

Exanthemata (eruptions caused e. g. by measles and other eruptive fevers) are treated as follows: tender leaves of neem (Azadirachta indica) and fine powder of the root of Glycyrrhiza glabra (*marutam*) are made in equal proportions into pills of pepper size. 1-2 pills with juice of sacred basil (Ocimum sanctum) and honey can be given thrice daily for 7-10 days. For skin lesions, a paste of neem leaves and turmeric powder should be applied externally. There is also treatment for psoriasis, both external and interal, for loss of hair, etc.

Some Siddha texts prescribe treatment even for such grave conditions as leucoderma, leprosy and skin-cancer. These treatments are naturally not cures. However, Siddha attitude vis-à-vis skin disease is holistic: the aim of the physician should be to treat the organism as a whole, not to be limited only to skin lesions as according to the Siddha view, most skin diseases are secondary to internal derangements. Hence exposure to sun-light, applying medicinal oil etc. goes hand in hand with proper diet, internal drugs and, e.g. letting out some quantity of blood by which procedure the toxic state of the system is temporarily minimized (e.g. in treatment of acute psoriasis, eczema, toxic erythema).

5. *Dental care*

Compared to Westerners, the teeth and gingivas of Indians are generally in much better and healthier condition. To some extent this is probably due to eating habits (prevailing vegetarianism). However, one of the main reasons for this state of affairs is the fact that in India regular brushing of teeth and tongue with twigs from certain plants is recommended and indeed generally practiced. According to *Patarttakuna cintamani* 1323, the following five trees should be used for brushing twigs: Acacia arabica Willd., Melia azadirachta, Ficus bengalensis, Achyranthes aspera, Phyllanthus reticulatus. Various other sources, textual and oral, add a number of yet other plants.[16]

Since we would strongly recommend this chapter of Siddha medical knowledge and skills to western dentists for study, details about the various plants used as brushes and for tooth-powders are given below.

1. Acacia arabica Willd. (*vel, karuvel*): root-bark is astringent; it contains tannin (12-20%). Burnt bark with burnt almond shell is powdered and mixed with salt to make good tooth powder.

2. Melia azadirachta (margosa, neem, *vempu*): astringent bark is a good bitter tonic. Tannin occurs in outer portion of bark. Nimbidin (bitter component in neem oil) is efficacious in bleeding gums etc.; an anti-bacterial principle in the leaf extract has been reported. Dried and powdered tender leaves form excellent tooth powder.

3. Ficus bengalensis (*al*): bark is a tonic and astringent. Contains tannin and anti-bacterial principles.

4. 'Triple powder' made of Terminalia chebula (*katukkay*, chebulic myrobalan) with tannic acid content of 20-40%, Terminalica bellerica (belleric myrobalan, *tanri*) with fruits containing 17% of tannin substance, and Phyllanthus emblica (emblic myrobalan, *nelli*) with fruits, bark and leaves rich in tannin and fruits as rich source of vitamin C (successfully used in treatment of scurvy) clears inflammation of gingiva and strengthens the gums.

5. Powdered bark of Terminalia arjuna (*marutu*), astringent, containing tannin, is used as tooth powder. In addition, Indians use calcium silicate as good tooth powder. They also regularly massage the gingiva, and clean the surface of their tongues. The text quoted above recommends that after brushing the teeth with a twig carefully and leisurely, the same piece of twig can be split lengthwise and used for tongue cleaning. Coarse things like stone, sand, straw and metals will destroy the dentine and gingiva, and should not be used for cleaning the

---

[16] A popular Tamil saying is *alum velum pallukkuruti* 'Ficus and Acacia strengthen the teeth.'

teeth. Also, chewing and biting stimulates and strengthens the teeth and gingiva and aids digestion. [17]

Among specific drugs used in Siddha dental care, only several selected remedies will be quoted.

a) Prophylactic and curative medicine for pyorrhoea, inflammation of gingiva and bad breath: Areca-nut is fried and mixed with equal quantity of rock salt (*intuppu*), Carum copticum ('bishop's weed', *omam*), Acacia catechu typica and alum. All five ingredients are powdered and used as tooth powder.

b) Oil extracted by distillation from clove is used externally against tooth-ache.

c) Salt-water gargle is a common remedy in inflammatory conditions of gingiva and throat.

d) Against mobility of tooth and tooth-ache, use a decoction prepared from bark of Eugenia jambolana (jamoon plum) as a gargle.

6. Surgery

In Siddha system of medicine, surgical methods are termed *acuravaittiyam / acuramaruttuvam*, lit. 'treatment [according to] demons'.[18] Surgery is classified into three major groups: *aruvai* (lit. 'cutting'), i.e. surgery proper, *akkini* (lit. 'fire', application of heat) and *karam* (lit. 'pungency; caustic'), removing tissues by other methods. [19]

1. Surgery proper refers to methods of using the knife and other surgical instruments, but also some other techniques. Most frequent among these are incision (Tamil *kiral*) used to let off pus, blood, etc., draining the blood (*kuruti vankal*) from the veins to cure certain diseases, enema (*piccal*) and 'blowing' (*utal*) when vapours are blown into ears and nose. Very frequent was leech application to evacuate blood or serum from affected parts of the body. Leeches were applied for chronic headaches and migraine, filariasis, pains due to severe inflammations, abscesses, and even mental disorders. The patient should be given food

---

[17] Cf. the popular Tamil saying, 'He who eats while chewing properly may live to be a hundred.'

[18] Under the term *acurar* (Sanskrit *asura-*) we must not imagine 'our' Western devils. The Hindu asuras are rather titans, anti-gods, giants at constant war with the gods. They are taught and presided by planet Venus.

[19] The Siddha surgical works available are *Akattiyar rana perunul, Akastiyar nayanaviti* and *Nakamuni nayanaviti*.

prior to the treatment, and the area of application had to be cleaned with alkaline earth and red ochre. Hairs had to be removed. Leeches should be applied only in Summer and before noon. Massages (*tokkatam*) for neurological disorders (paraplegia, hemiplegia, paralysis etc.) after application of medicated oils and creams are also mentioned.

2. Heat application is performed in various forms: vapour (produced by boiling drugs in water or specific oils), fomentation (with cloth dipped in hot water or medicated oils), direct heat with the help of earthen vessels, metals, sun, and a specific treatment when drugs are mixed, packed in cloth, and put in orifices like the ear, nose, etc. Thus e.g. black cumin seeds are used against sinusitis, garlic and asafoetida in treatment of ear disorders, and Terminalia chebula with Ficus glomerata in treatment of vaginal ulcers.

3. Destroyed tissues in ulcers etc. are removed with the application of oil, powder, ointment or paste. Finally, the famous Akattiyar is credited to have performed trephination of the skull to remove a toad (*terai*) from the brain of his pupil Teraiyar (hence the disciple's name).

7. Siddha treatment for poisons

[While the present author conducted (repeatedly between 1968 -1981) research in the languages and cultures of Nilgiri tribes, he encountered cases of poisonous bites by reptiles, centipedes, scorpions etc., and made acquaintance, in Ootacamund, with a Siddha practitioner who specialized in treatment of such cases. The present account is based on this information as well as on data gathered from several other informants and by N. Jaganathan, M. A., of Government College, Ooty.]

The whole procedure of treatment consists of four steps: diagnosis, therapy by reciting magic spells, therapy by oral administration of antidotes, and external / invasive therapy.

It is first necessary to determine the kind of reptile or other animal/insect which caused the bite. In the case of poisonous snakes this is determined by smelling the bitten spot. If it smells of Pandanus odoratissimus (fragrant screw-pine) flower, it was a cobra; if of Bignonia chelonoides (trumpet flower), it was Lycoden Aulicus; if of tamarind flower, it was viper; if of jasmine flower, it was earth snake; if of pepper or dry ginger, it was small snake; etc. Snakes which have fangs have two poisonous teeth in front, both in upper and lower portion of the mouth. These teeth are bent inward, and hollow with canals. Immediately after the bite, the poisonous fluid is secreted through the canals from the poison glands into the muscle of the victim; the poison is carried by blood into the system and may cause death. It is maintained that if the bite was due to only one of the teeth, cure is well possible. If it was due to all four teeth, the poison will affect the central nervous system within 32 hours, and cure will be very difficult. In the case of a one-tooth bite the poison may infect only the skin, and this will be cured by herbal medicine; in the case of a two-teeth bite, it will affect the flesh, and this too can be cured by herbal medicines plus some additional procedures; in the case of a three-teeth bite, the poison will have touched the bones; cure is difficult but possible; in case of four-teeth bite, the brain will be affected and survival is rare.

Treatment.

Before administering the complex anti-venom drug (see below) the following steps are necessary:

1. Tie a rope immediately above the bite.
2. Make the victim drink (his own) urine.
3. Give him eat flowers / leaves of Calotropis gigantea.
4. Crush betel leaves, salt and pepper, soak in girl's urine for a male victim and in boy's urine for female, filter the liquid and put a few drops in the eyes, ears and nostrils. Blow through a pipe inside the ears.
5. Make the victim drink water mixed with alum powder.

Specific medicine: Take pepper, garlic, asafoetida, nut of Strychnos nux vomica, seeds of Strychnos potatorum, nut of Randia durnetorum and jasmine bark in equal proportions, crush these, put them in a mud receptacle with goat's urine, leave it standing for 8 days, grind on 9th day with the same urine, soak with it a cloth, dry it in cowdung smoke, keep it ready. For all kinds of poison, tear a one-inch-by-three-inches piece of this cloth and pound it finely. Soak this in juice of Indigofera tincturia, and let a few drops into each nostril.

Another method of treatment, used by native doctors who deal with emergency cases of snake, scorpion etc. bites is as follows:

1. Mix 5 grams of alum powder in 100 ml water, give this mixture to drink. 2. Tighten a rope above the site of the bite. 3. Crush betel leaves, pepper and salt in (anyone's) urine, filter it, let a few drops into eyes, nose and ears. 4. During this procedure, a *mantravadin* (person who knows specific spells) should repeat mantras holding a bunch of margosa leaves rapidly shaking it and whipping the victim vigorously from head to foot.

5. As food, give rice porridge without salt.

6. Induce purging.

7. Grind bark of Indigofera root, mix with neem oil sediments, give it twice, morning and evening, for 3 days, with salt-free diet.

Some specific procedures derived from medieval Siddha texts:

Akattiyar Kaumati nul 400, 45-8:

Grind white-headed kite's head, claws, eye-balls and beak with front teeth of the mongoose, its eye-balls, brain and nose, add milk of 2 plants (Calotropis gigantea and Cynanchum viminale), make pills the size of a liquorice seed, dry them in shade. For any severe poisoning, rub half a pill in urine of a little girl for a male victim, and in boy's urine for a female victim, administer it to swallow. The poison will 'come down'. When the victim is in comatose state, insert a copper tube into renal canal and pour in the medicine. If the victim is a female, insert the same treatment through the vagina. The patient will awake 'as if from sleep'.

There are prescribed treatments for the bite of a cat, rabid dog or fox, centipede, scorpion, for wasp sting, bee sting, etc.

8. Simple Siddha medicines for daily use.

A large number of Siddha drugs is used for minor ailments and in prophylaxis. They are easily obtainable, easily prepared, and present no danger. Hence they are used in Tamil homes in day-to-day use, often the knowledge, derived from Siddha tradition, is carried on by the old women of the house / village.

Indigestion, including nausea, headache, flatulence etc:

The simplest remedy is ginger juice mixed with fresh lemon juice sweetened with honey taken on empty stomach. Ginger (Zingiber officinale) acts as stimulant, carminative and digestant; it is also anti-flatulent. Lemon (Citrus aurantifolia) is an appetizer, digestant, good anti-emetic agent and liver stimulant, as well as an anti-inflammatory agent (high vitamin C content).

Another, more complex drug, a 'granny's preparation', a household remedy for all problems due to indigestion, is made as follows (it is well known as *perunkaya curanam*): boil shortly the following ingredients: asafoetida (anti-flatulent), common salt (antibacterial), cumin and caraway seeds (chologogue, stimulant and appetizer), bishop's weed (Carum copticum; antiemetic, liver tonic) and 'three pungents' (dry ginger, black pepper, long pepper; digestant, stimulant, vasodilator, muscle relaxant, carminative), and give to drink.

Constipation:

Siddha sources quote as many as six remedies:

1. Daily intake of honey in warm water taken early morning on empty stomach (laxative, soothing, anti-inflammatory effects).
2. Tender chebulic myrobalan taken as decoction at bed time.
3. Decoction of grapes of wine (Vitis vinifera).
4. Against long-standing constipation: mixed powdered tender chebulic myrobalan with castor oil.
5. When laxative fails, one must apply enema: juice of Aloe barbadensis with castor oil.
6. Milk and honey with rock salt solution is also used as enema.

Diarrhoea

Excellent remedy against non-specific diarrhoea: Dry ginger powder plus powdered black pepper, in equal parts taken with water and honey 3-4 times relieves diarrhoea due to indigestion.

Chronic tonsilitis (repeated infection of tonsils)

Paste of garlic mixed with honey applied as throat swab.

Burns and scalds due to dry or wet heat

Turmeric and margosa leaves ground and applied with honey as paste: antiseptic, anti-bacterial, anti-inflammatory, soothing. Prevents blister-formation.

Siddha medicine used as prophylactic

According to the Siddha tradition, the following vegetables should be eaten in plenty:

a. Drumstick leaves (Moringa oleifera): excellent source of vitamin A.

b. Eclipta alba and Phyllanthus niruri: regenerative of liver cells, prophylactic against liver disorders (cholagogue action, liver tonic).

c. Spinach. Good source of vitamin B complex in addition to phosphorus and calcium content. Prevents urinary disorders.

d. Cucumber, radish (Raphanus sativus), pumpkin (Benincasa), plantain skin: all indicated in urinary disorders. In addition, radish and plantain skin are helpful in hypertensive cardiac disease.

e. Lemon as digestant, appetizer, antiflatulent and liver tonic has been mentioned.

f. Garlic: antiflatulent, digestant, lactogogue, liver stimulant, antiseptic. Proved anti-cholesterol and anti-rheumatic activity. Excellent bactericidal.

The basic Siddha attitude towards drugs is expressed by an old saying which emphasizes the use of herbs (leaves, stems, roots); if these are not effective, gradual use of metals and minerals is recommended: 'Consider roots, consider leaves; if they remain (ineffective), consider carefully metals and minerals.'

Recipe: Palpitations of the heart.

Drink daily before retiring a cup of warm milk with a teaspoon of honey. Specific remedy: To be taken daily in the morning: A small piece of ground ginger mixed with 4 oz. of hot water should be left standing for half-an-hour; strain and mix with one teaspoon of honey and the juice of half lemon.

Recipe: Sexual weakness.

Regular and frequent intercourse. Oral-genital sex: visualize yourself as the passively creative Siva, and your partner as your sakti-energy. Let her lie upon you and drink your semen (*cukkilam*); let you suck her secretion of pleasure (*curatanir*).

WARNING:

Readers are urgently warned not to experiment on their own with the prescriptions, recipes and suggestions contained in this publication.

7
Yoga In Siddha Tradition

This part of the book is very short for three reasons: First, yoga, for the Siddhas, is far from being either the goal they aim for, or their main preoccupation. It is in the Siddha tradition one of the means how to foster the body, gain perpetual health, and reach 'immortality' (by which read 'extreme longevity'). Second, the main purpose of this book is to deal with the overall Siddha search of that goal, mostly, however, in the field of Siddha medicine. And, finally, the yoga part of Siddhism has been dealt with sufficiently in the 1973 (1993) publication.[1] Nevertheless, a basic understanding of one part of yoga, viz. of Tantrik-oriented Hatha Yoga, is necessary for understanding of the Siddha tradition as such, in particularly of its medicine, but also of the Siddha poetry.[2]

---

1 Op.cit. chapter 6, pp.37 - 59.

2 Such basic understanding can be (only) partly gained by the study of selected texts mentioned in this chapter. However, intellectual grasp is not sufficient. One can never understand yoga completely from 'outside'; it has to be 'performed', to be done with one's entire 'body-mind'.This should be so obvious that it sounds almost banal, and yet one reads and hears 'experts' talking about things like yoga, zen or meditation on the basis of reading a few books.

Hatha Yoga is considered by the Siddha tradition to have a double function: first and foremost, it is one of the methods to enhance physical health and 'eternal' youth. Second, and this is important, too, it is a physiological preparation for *samyama*, that is, for meditation.

The supreme end to achieve is, however, not splendid health and 'eternal' youth. Even that is only a means to an end: the true aim of Siddha Yoga is liberation, rebirth to a non-conditioned mode of being. And this end can be achieved - so the Siddhas have maintained - by a complex method consisting of several components: a healthy daily regime, the application of Siddha medical knowledge for prevention and cure, ascetic techniques and meditation - that is, by yoga. In this sense, and in this sense only, all Tamil Siddhas are yogins.

The Yoga of Siddha tradition corresponds to the well-described techniques of Hatha Yoga. The first step in this physical discipline are the *asanas* (Tamil *irukkai*), that is various postures in which the subject is able 'to rest immobile for a long time and without effort'[3]. They have, in Siddha Yoga, a triple function: immobilizing body for concentration and meditation; therapeutic value; and magical value. Accompanying the postures are *bandhas* (contractions pertaining to muscles or groups of muscles)[4] and *mudras* or 'gestures' (often accompanied by mantras, i.e. spells or oral formulae of great magic power)[5]. Controlled breathing (*pranayama*) is the next step in yoga discipline. We must realize that *prana* is not just respiratory breath but vital force that moves not only living bodies, but the whole universe; it is cosmic breath, manifestation of Cosmic Consciousness, of the Absolute Void. Hence yoga breathing technique represents, in its expiratory phase, the destruction of discursive, intellectual knowledge - source of delusion; in the phase of inspiration, the acquisition of the conviction of the subject's identity with the Cosmic Void; and in arresting the breath, the concentration on that conviction. However, in the Siddha tradition, breath-control is only an aid, just as the entire sphere of yogic techniques. It has been established by modern experiments that there exists an intimate, as yet not quite

---

3 Yogadarsana II.46.

4 E.g. *mulabandha* 'anal contraction' of anal sphincters to arrest the flow of semen.

5 E.g. *khecimudra*, arresting expiration by the tongue, preceded by forceful inspiration, used for the stopping of breath.

understood, connection between controlled breathing and many psychosomatic phenomena.[6]

As stressed above, Hatha Yoga is, for the Siddhas, one of the methods of gaining liberation which is understood as the conquest of 'immortality' in this life. The sign of absolute and true liberation is, for the Siddhas, a physical body aglow with the fire of immortality.[7]

Anyone who wishes to get acquainted theoretically with yoga in general, including its philosophical background, origins, history, development and ideology, should read the detailed and profound book by Mircea Eliade, *Yoga, Immortality and Freedom* (1st ed., New York, 1958, 2nd, Princeton, 1969). For those who wish to make themselves familiar with Hatha Yoga in terms of a practical guide to Yogic discipline, two no-nonsense authentic books can be recommended to Western readers: Swami Vishnudevananda, *The Complete Illustrated Book of Yoga* (introduction Dr Marcus Bach) (Pocket Books, New York, 1972), and Richard Hittleman, *Yoga for Physical Fitness* (2nd printing, Prentice Hall, 1966). A few additional titles are given below in the footnote.[8] Since this work is above all about the physiological and medical knowledge, theory and practice, of the Tamil Siddhas, one should stress in any discussion of Hatha Yoga the fact that the physiological authenticity of phenomena which had for a long time been considered impossible or doubtful (or even faked) has been established on the basis of controlled experiments by scientists educated in terms of modern critical medicine. Such experiments were performed by both Indian and Western (French, German, Italian etc.) physicians and published. They include the control of neurovegetative system, respiratory and cardiac rhythms, the ability to pump and expel liquids by the urethra (or the rectum), arrest of seminal emission (and even 'return of semen') etc. A select bibliography on this topic is given in the footnote.[9].

---

6 See below, ftn.9.

7 Uromarisi nanam 12. Also, some poems by Ramalinga Svami.

8 Garrison, Omar, *Tantra, the Yoga of Sex*, Avon Books, New York, 1973 (1st ed.1964); Stearn, J., *Yoga, Youth, and Reincarnation*, New York, 1968; Theos, Bernard, *Hatha-Yoga, The Report of a Personal Experience*, New York, 1944.

9 Anand, B.K., China, G.S., 'Investigations on Yogis claiming to stop their heart beats', Ind. Journal of Medical Research 49, 1.1.1961, 90-

4; Bagchi, B.K., Wenger, M.A. 'Corrélations électrophysiologiques des certains exercises yogiques', Compte rendu, 1er Congrès international des sciences neurologiques de Bruxelles, 21.- 28.6.1957, Vol.3, Pergamon Press, 1959; Brosse, T., Etudes expérimentales des techniques du Yoga, Expérimentation psychosomatique, Ecole française d'Extrême-Orient, Paris, 1963; Das, M.N., Gastaut, H., 'Variations de l'activité électrique de cerveau, du coeur et des muscles squelettiques au cours de la méditation et de l'extase yogique', Conditionnement et réactivité en électroencephalographie, Paris, Masson, 1957, 211-18; Filliozat, J., 'Les limites des pouvoirs humains dans l'Inde', Limites de l'humain, Paris, 1943, 23-8; Laubry, Ch., Brosse, T., 'Documents recueillies aux Indes sur les "yogins" par l'enregistrement simultané du pouls, de la respiration et de l'électrocardiogramme'. Presse medicale, Paris, LXXXIII, 14 October 1936; Satyanarayanamurti, G.V., M.D., Brahmayya, P., Sastri, M.B., B.S., 'A preliminary scientific investigation into some of the unusual manifestations acquired as a result of Yogic practices in India', Wiener Zeitschrift für Nervenheilkunde und deren Grenzgebiete, Wien, Springer, 1958. For Indian medicine in general, cf. Bhishagacarya, G.M., *History of Indian Medicine*, 2 vols, Calcutta, 1923-26; Filliozat, J., *La doctrine classique de la médicine indienne*, Paris, 1949; Jolly, J., *Indian Medicine*, Poona, 1951 (orig. ed. *Indische Medizin*, Strassburg, 1901); Sanyal, P.K., *A Story of Medicine and Pharmacy in India*, Calcutta, 1964; Zimmer, H.R., *Hindu Medicine*, Baltimore, 1948.

8. Daily Regime

Terayar, in his treatise on hygiene entitled *Noyanukaviti* (The Manner How to Prevent Illness), unfortunately preserved only in fragments,[1] gives the following advice on overall daily regime (these verses are often quoted as quintessence of Siddha medical wisdom):

He who gives free way to alvine discharges,[2]
he who does not indulge in excess in sex,[3]
he who at meals drinks boiled water,
dilutes one's yoghurt with water, and
uses only melted butter[4]

---

1 Teraiyar (probably of 15th century), according to tradition student of Akattiyar. Prolific writer on subjects connected with his profession as skillful healer. Works: *Cikamanivenpa*, treatise on medicine; *Natikkottu*, treatise on pulse; *Noyanukaviti* (fragmentary) on hygiene. There is a number of legendary stories current about him. Ascribed to him are yet other works: *Maruttupparatam, Manivenpa, Tailavarukkaccurukkam, Nirkkurineykkuri castiram* and also and especially *Patarttakuna cintamani* (cf. A. Singaravelu Mudaliar, *Abithana Chintamani*, reprint New Delhi, 1981, p.891).

2 Alvine discharges refers to the stool. Prevention of constipation is given very important place in Siddha hygiene.

3 But there is another stream in Siddha tradition which recommends frequent and variegated sexual activity, see one of the following chapters on Siddha attitude to sex.

4 Yoghurt: Tamil *mor* 'curdled milk; yoghurt'; to be eaten only diluted with water; melted butter: Tam. *ney*, ghee.

at the very mention of his name disease will depart.
We will eat only twice, not three times a day.[5]
We will sleep only at night, not during the daytime.[6]
We will have sex only once in a month.[7]
We will drink water only at meals even if thirsty.
We will not eat tubers of any plant except of karanai.[8]
We will not eat unripe fruits except the tender plantain.
We will take a short walk after each friendly meal.
What has then death to do with us?
Once every six months we will take an emetic.[9]
We will take purgative once in four months.[10]
Once in a month and a half, we will take naciyam.[11]
We will have the head shaved twice in a fortnight.
Once every fourth day we'll anoint ourselves with oil and bathe.
We will apply collyrium[12] to the eyes every third day.
We will never smell perfumes or flowers in the middle of the night.
What has then death to do with us?

---

5 All streams of Siddha tradition recommend frugality and temperance in food habits. A well-known Tamil proverb says, 'He who eats once [a day] is a yogin (*yoki*); he who eats twice is a happy man (*poki*); he who eats three times is a sick man (*roki*); he who eats four times is a sinner (*pavi*).'

6 There is a well-known Siddha saying, 'Sleep during daytime is forbidden.' Siddha tradition is very strict about this.

7 Some sources also forbid intercourse during daytime. Most Siddha texts of this temperate tradition recommend sexual intercourse once a week. Unnecessary spilling of semen is believed to reduce the faculty of memory and provoke general weakness.

8 Most probably the medical plant *Arum minutum*, but could also be a tuberous-rooted herb, *Amorphophattus campanulatus*; or Tahiti arrowroot (*Tacca pinnatifida*), or *Arum macrorhyzon* (tuberous-rooted herb).

9 Tamil *vamanamaruntu*, lit. 'vomiting medicine'.

10 Tamil *petiyurai*, lit. 'diarrhoea-food'.

11 A medicine prepared from the juice of certain herbs, taken by the nose to promote discharge of mucus (cf. Sanskrit *nasya* - Engl. 'nose').

12 Liquid pigment dropped into eye to form a dark attractive residue on the rim.

9.
Siddha Alchemy

If there is not much literature on Siddha *vaittiyam* (medicine), on Siddha alchemy - *racavatam*[1] - there is practically nothing. There exist of course several treatises in Tamil, such as Hakim Mukammatu Aptulla's *Racavata cintamani*, but these texts are either in palmleaf manuscripts, or out of print, and in any case almost inaccessible.

What was the kind of alchemy the Siddhas occupied themselves with? And why can many Siddhas of the past be designated as alchemists?[2]

Alchemy is described as 'the medieval forerunner of chemistry, esp. seeking to turn base metals into gold or silver.'[3] Does this definition

---

1 From Sanskrit *rasavada* - 'transmuting baser metals into gold; alchemy'; cf. Tam. *iracavati* 'alchemist'; connected with *iracam* 'mercury'. Cf.also *iracayanam* < *rasayana* - 'elixir of life; medicine credited to have the property of prolonging life and preventing ageing'.

2 Here it is indeed legitimate to use past tense, since in our days there is no more any living tradition of Siddha alchemy, in sharp contrast to Siddha medicine. Another reason why this chapter of the book is so short.

3 *The Concise Oxford Dictionary,* Eighth Edition 1990, *s.v.* Not very successful definition, and certainly far from universal. The academic view on alchemy and magic is changing rapidly, see S J Tambiah, *Magic, Science, Religion and the Scope of Rationality* (C.U.P 1990).

apply to Siddha alchemy? Yes and no. Yes in the sense that Siddha alchemists were obviously also preoccupied with the transmutation of base metals into gold. Why gold? Because 'gold is immortality',[4] because it is *the* perfect metal, and stands as such as a symbol of spiritual perfection and deathlessness.

However, Siddha alchemy was no pre-science, no 'medieval chemistry', no pre-chemistry.[5] It was rather a spiritual technique, operating - in full agreement with Siddha doctrines - on matter. Another reason for the Siddha interest in alchemy was the doctrine of the homogenization of human body and cosmic matter. The contemplation of one's 'subtle' body (*nunnutal*) as 'cosmicised' leads to one's preoccupation with the transformation of substances (*carakku*) - in other words, with alchemy.

Moreover, one of the main reasons of Siddha medical practice, and here there is a close and direct contact with alchemy broadly conceived, is the transmutation of one's 'gross' physical body (*paruvutal*) into incorruptible substance, so that one's body achieves 'eternal' health, 'immortality', or at least enormous longevity.[6]

Finally, there was an important agreement between Siddha Yoga and medicine, and in fact the whole philosophy of the Siddhas, and alchemy, at least in one aspect of approach: Siddha doctrines (whether Yogic, medical, or philosophical) and alchemy stand in opposition to purely discursive knowledge, purely speculative methods, to metaphysics for metaphysics' sake. The Siddhas are experimental pragmatists, they work with matter as well as with spirit, with the entire body-mind. 'Just as the *cittar* work on their body, so they also work on matter - to finish it, to make it mature, perfect (like their body), to change it into gold ... There is thus an occult correspondence between matter and man's psychophysical body',[7] and between Siddha Yoga and Siddha alchemy.

---

4 Cf. *Satapathabrahmana* III.8.27 and elsewhere: *amrtam ayur hiranyam*.

5 M.Eliade, *Yoga, Immortality and Freedom*, Princeton, 1969, p.281.

6 Cf.the following chapter on longevity and 'immortality'. Attempts to transmute the body by means of *rasapana* elixir composed mainly of mercury and mica (symbols of Siva and Gauri) are dealt with below. Cf. also the fact that the Indian term for alchemy is, literally, 'science of mercury'.

7 The 1973 (1993) publication, p. 36.

10. Rejuvenation, Longevity and 'Immortality'

If body is destroyed, soul is destroyed,
and one won't attain the true knowledge of power.
Having acquired the skill to foster the body,
I cherished the body, and I fostered the soul.
Medicine means: prevent the body's illness.
Medicine means: prevent the mind's illness.
Medicine's purpose is to avert disease.
Hence medicine is the prevention of death.
(Tirumular, *Tirumantiram* 800)

On the pure Path of the Absolute
I learned the science of deathlessness.
(Ramalinga Svami)

One definition of the Siddhas could be 'South Indian, in particular Tamil sages who have accepted as their basic doctrine the indissoluble unity of body and spirit, and proclaimed as their method of liberation the search for physical immortality'. Out of this description of Siddha tradition follows its preoccupation with the art and science of the prevention and cure of disease and, specifically, their dream of discovering and employing a drug which would bring about rejuvenation and prolong life, if possible, indefinitely. This particular preoccupation is termed in Siddha parlance *kayacitti*, literally magic power (*citti*) [over] the body (*kayam*),[1] and the drug which would have the power of rejuvenating the body and prolong life is termed *kaya-karpam (< kayakalpa)*.

The *kayakarpam* treatment consists in the following steps:

1. Preservation of vital energy by influencing internal secretions and blood circulation through controlled breathing and Yoga practice.

2. Conservation of male semen and female secretion, to use it in regenerating processes.

3. Use of a 'universal' salt known as *muppu / muppuu*, prepared by special processes to induce rejuvenation.

4. Use of (calcinated) powders prepared from metals and minerals such as mercury, sulphur, gold, mica, copper, iron, etc.

5. Use of drugs prepared from herbs.

This last step (5) is the one most often employed as it is the safest, and these drugs are relatively easily obtained, whereas step (4) is most risky, and hence its 'secrets' are relatively well and jealously guarded.

Each Siddha author and each Siddha physician and healer has his own *kayakalpa* plant. Tanvantiri (cf. Tanvantiri vaittiyam) mentions Indian gooseberry (emblic myrobalan), aloes, root of the vilvam (bael, Crataeva) etc.; Pokar talks of asparagus, aloes, root of bael etc.; Tirumular mentions fresh and dry ginger, Teraiyar prefers lime fruit, holy basil, margosa etc., and a text known as *Nanacastirattirattu* speaks of five plants which purify the body and induce rejuvenation (among them cloves, pepper and cumin). In what follows, some of these plants which have been studied relatively recently in the *Government Siddha Dispensary*[2] will be discussed in some detail. As mentioned above, these remedies, while considered to be powerful, are relatively harmless and mostly without side-effects, and may be tried by anyone.

---

[1] Cf. the expressions *kayacittiyanon* 'one who has attained the power of *kayacitti*'; *kayacitticcunam*, crystallized or foliated gypsum used as medicine. Interestingly enough, urine salt is designated as *kayacittiyuppu*.

[2] By Dr. G. Geetha, M.D., at Chepauk, Madras 600 005.

1. **Cyperus rotundus** (Tamil *korai*, Telugu and Kannada *tunga*). An aquatic plant praised by all Siddhas as effective with rejuvenating powers. Teraiyar says, 'Just like god Kumaran who shields the gods from the arrows of antigods, so this drug has the power of protecting men from every disease'. Its root *koraik-kilanku* should be powdered and taken with melted butter and the root of Artemis pyrthrum (Tam. *akkarakaram*). Thus taken, it is a cure for pulmonary disease. Modern research has shown that it has anti-inflammatory, antipyretic and analgesic properties. Clinical trials found that it helped in spasmodic pains in the uterus and that it effectively cured conjunctivitis.

2. **Indian aloes** (Tamil *karralai*) has been praised by a number of Siddhas who in their *paribhasha* (professional coded language) call it *kumari*, i.e. 'young maiden' because of its rejuvenating properties.[3] According to Agastyar, aloe bestows longevity, youth and vigour. In Siddha medicine, it is used for the cure of peptic ulcers, but also in cases of conjunctivitis, and for hair growth. Modern research has found vitamin A besides a long list of ingredients, pectin, calcium, magnesium, phosphate, nitrate, glucoprotein, aminoacids, etc.

3. **Phyllanthus Niruri** (*kilanelli*) is useful in urinary infections and is employed in treatment of sexually transmitted diseases and skin diseases. It contains iron, flavin, calcium, and alcaloids effective in cure of liver disorders.

4. **Hydrocotyle Asiatica** (*vallarai*). This is mentioned by all Siddhas as rejuvenating drug which can be consumed as food. It contains steroids, glycosides, aminoacids, tannic acid, sugar, anorganic salts, etc., and from its ash were isolated magnesium, sodium, iron, calcium and phosphates. It is used in diseases of the blood, sexually transmitted diseases and skin diseases, but also as a tonic for memory and the nervous system.

5. **Crataeva religiosa** (vilvam, bael). Almost all parts of the tree - leaves, roots, and green and ripe fruit - have medicinal properties. Fruits can be pickled. From all parts one can make decoction as general tonic

---

3 The other two Indian medical systems, Ayurvedic and Unani, mention also this plant as positively efficient. In ancient Tamil literature, a long poem called Perumpanarruppatai ('The Long Poem For the Bard With Lute', c.200 A.D.) mentions in line 247 a plant by name of *kumari*, used as pesticide. The Bible (John XIX.39) mentions Nicodem who brought a mixture of myrrh and aloes to preserve the body of Jesus.

for the brain, in cases of dysentery and impotence, and as heart stimulant. The root, bark and leaves contain tannic acid, the ash contains potassium, phosphates of lime, iron, calcium, magnesium, etc.

6. **Eclipta alba** (Tam. *karicalai*). A number of Siddhas have mentioned its rejuvenating properties. Agastyar says it is good in cases of sore throat, cough, jaundice, dropsy and anaemia. Other works maintain that it improves intelligence. Even Tirumular mentions it as maintaining youthfulness. According to medieval Tamil inscriptions, during the period of imperial Cholas it was cultivated on large scale and taxed. It is quoted in a number of modern (English-language) pharmacographias of India (dated 1890, 1891, 1896, 1899, 1956).

7. **Juice of the root of fresh ginger** (*inciver*, whence the Greek and Latin terms zingiberos, English ginger, Italian zenzovero, Czech zázvor etc.!), and dry ginger (*cukku*) are recommended in all Siddha texts. As a rejuvenating drug it should be taken in the mornings and at noon. Tiruvalluvar's Karpam 300 says clearly, 'in the morning fresh ginger, at noon dry ginger'.[4] This has become a popular saying. It contains volatile oils, resin, starch, etc. With lemon / lime juice, dry ginger is used as good heart tonic.

8. **Azadirachta indica** (*vempu*, margosa) was preferred by Teran who mentions it several times. All its parts have medicinal value: its dry flowers contain a fatty acid and other components which can cure ulcers. Fresh flowers are used in lung infections. The bark contains tannin, nimbidin, etc.; the oil is rich in acids, glycosides, sulphur, resins. The gum contains glucouronic acid, galactopyranose and galactose, and is used against impotence. The plant is also a bacteriostat.

According to Siddha practice, while one is on *kayakalpa* (rejuvenating) diet, certain general principles should be observed. A few food items should be avoided: gingilly oil, fish, mutton and foodstuffs rich in calcium (according to a much stricter regime, the only permitted diet consists of rice-pudding, pepper, cow's butter, sugar and milk). In contrast, certain items should be taken in plenty: pepper, cumin seeds, curry leaves, lime juice, Bengal gram, cow's ghee, greens in general. It is stated that rejuvenation or the attainment of *kayacitti* before the age of forty is best, although it can be done up to the age of eighty.[5] The best

---

4 *kalayil inci katumpakal cukku.*

5 This lengthy note contains the case-history of a retired district and sessions judge from Madras who had undergone a rejuvenation treatment provided by

months for such treatment are Cittirai (roughly April-May), Vaikaci (May-June), Aipaci (October-November) and Karttikai (November-December).[6]

---

a Siddha sadhu. It is given here to present a rough idea (by no means reliable, generally valid or critically evaluated!) of the circumstances of such treatment. The person in question had passed the age of sixty. He wished to try the 'much acclaimed rejuvenating medicine' and, eager to test the truth of it, for he found the Siddha processes 'all veiled in obscure terminology coined by them', and he searched for someone who would oblige. A sadhu who was staying in his house left beyond a 'paste' stating that it was the elixir. When the judge neared 65, he decided to consume the drug, in spite of the warning by some Siddha informants that there would follow violent reactions in the body. 'I started taking it one grain in the morning and another in the evening in honey from 5th May 1973 and continued it for forty-eight days.' He did not follow any diet restrictions (against the advice of the Siddhas), and 'everything appeared to be smooth going'. 'On the 52nd day trouble started . . . All the limbs of my body started twisting and aching . . .Within a few minutes thereafter acute diarrhoea and temperature started. Within 3 hours I purged thirty times, but there was no vomiting. I fell down unconscious. I regained consciousness after eighteen hours. Examination of my body by eminent doctors showed normal and sound heart, healthy lungs and blood pressure absolutely normal (120 / 80).' (In 1971, his blood pressure was between 110 - 180 / 210). 'For about 10 days after I regained my consciousness I was purging blood. I refused to take any medicine either allopathic or Indian... Gradually diarrhoea and bleeding stopped. Thirty days had passed. But to my surprise I found the thick skin in my palms and feet started peeling off...Within 20 days the whole skin went off...Not a drop of blood appeared to be in my body. But within about two months fresh blood surged up in my body. The ...doctors were watching my progress with some surprise ...A month later my nails on all the fingers in the hands and legs started gradually being wasted and fresh nails appeared. All the old nails have gone off and new nails sprang up ... The skin pealed off, nails came away, and my [high] blood pressure had vanished. I do not know what else may happen. For the present, I feel I have no disease ...Only that much I can say at this stage.' (In V. Balaramiah, *The Art of Deathlessness*, Madras, 1974, 28 ...36). Most of the symptoms described seem to point to a violent poisoning by some inorganic stuff.

6 As interesting postscript one may note that according to the Siddhas' opinion, certain *kayakalpa* plants have the effect of improving sperm count and quality: thus asparagus, Hydrocotyle asiatica (*vallarai*) and the root of

The following discussion is very approximative and should be taken with a large grain of salt and with critical caution. It concerns the 'magic' drug leading to 'immortality' of the body, termed *muppu* (with the final -u short or long). All ancient Siddhas mentioned it, but command that one should not freely discuss it, this being the core of the Siddha 'secret' of rejuvenation. Modern Siddhas are very reticent, and what they say is rather contradictory. In fact, we do not have any clear and comprehensive critical description of the process of origin or manufacture of muppu. Even the term is obscure. Perhaps indeed it can be derived from the words for 'three' (*munru, mu-*) and 'salt' (*uppu*), although it is (linguistically) odd and not convincing. According to the text Curyanatar nanacuttiram (st. 3), the 'root components' of this magic stuff are moon-salt (*intu*), sun-salt (*iravi*) and fire-salt (*vanni*) whatever that may mean.[7] Another text, Pancarattinam 500 by Tiruvalluva Nayanar says that muppu is composed of *uvarnir*, i.e. 'salty / brackish water', *uvar mannuppu*, lit. 'salt of saline soil', but probably referring to salt of fullers' earth (crude carbonate of soda) and *cukkan*, so-called Kunkur lime-stone (impure concretionary carbonate of lime).This would well agree with the overall use in Siddha pharmacopoeia of inorganic stuff, but the trouble with all these terms is that they may belong to the Siddha professional jargon, hence be in fact metaphors for something else.

According to some modern Siddhas who follow ancient texts and are willing to discuss the matter, the sun-salt is identified with the following mineral stuff: limestone, sea-foam (*katalnurai*, Meerschaum), chalk. One could probably safely conclude that one of the 'three salts' of muppu is indeed limestone (*kalluppu*) in its many varieties, which contain large amount of calcium carbonate.[8] Moon-salt seems to be the saline efflorescence found in places of scanty rainfall and low humidity with high alkaline content and large excess of sodium salt. According to

---

amukkira (Withania somnifera, Indian winter cherry or Physalis flexuosa, Malayalam *amukkiram*, Kannada *amangura*).

7 According to one of my Siddha informants, this is Siddha code-language for substances derived from male sperm ('moon'), female secretion / menstrual blood ('sun') and urine ('fire') - a comment which may be rather doubtful. However, see above for the discussion of these substances.

8 Such is the conclusion reached by Dr. Andiappa Pillai of Madurai Kamaraj University.

Akattiyar (Ponnirukantam, Part 3, st. 16),[9] moon-salt (*vellaikkal*) and sun-salt are both found near each other in dry lands where even grass will not properly grow. It is known to washermen who use it in their work (Pancarattinam 500, st.72). The third salt is 'rock salt' (*parai uppu*).

Dr. Andiappa identifies rock-salt with sodium chloride , collected from sea water. According to him, in muppu, lime-stone is the source of calcium, rock-salt is chemically sodium chloride, and moon-salt is the source of potassium. 'The maintenance of a stable metabolism within the cell is due to the presence of these salts in the proper ratio in the fluid which surrounds the cell.' According to the above-quoted author, muppu 'is the best combination to bring the requisite equilibirum and the altered state of cell comes to normal'.[10]

Another hypothesis, based on both textual and oral transmission, seeks muppu alias muppu kuru in human organic matters of several kinds: urine, male sperm, female orgasmic fluid, amniotic fluid and menstrual blood. Several texts speak of *amurikarpam* which, literally, would mean 'the longevity-medicine of urine'. However, there is another term for 'urine', viz. *amari*; and a homophone, *amari*, is another designation for the aloe (*kumari*), mentioned above among plants which are used in the rejuvenation process. It is possible that a confusion of the two led to the notion of urine as a drug inducing longevity. Nevertheless, one's own fresh urine is known to have been consumed in India (not only within the Siddha tradition) not so long ago probably because of its mildly antiseptic properties.[11]

Male sperm and the exudation of moisture which covers the vulva before and during coitus have been recommended in some branches of

---

9 Cf.also Kurmanantar nanacuttiram 50, st. 32, and other texts ascribed to Akattiyar.

10 One word in addition for the linguistically-minded reader in connection with the term itself: both forms, *muppu* (with short -u) and *muppuu* (with long -u), occur in the texts. Tamil Lexicon (VI.3270) contains the form with the long vowel, deriving it from *mu-* 'three' + *uppu* 'salt', and says, 'A salt believed to have the power of transmuting base metals into gold, and to enable one to live 100,000 years '. However, some Siddhas derive this form with the long final vowel from the word for 'three' plus *pu* 'flower[s]', this term referring either to three most potent herbal drugs, or again, speaking metaphorically about substances connected with sex.

11 Cf.also the chapter entitled *amuritaranai* 'retaining of urine' in the third book of Tirumantiram.

Siddha Tantrik tradition as having rejuvenating effect. So has apparently their mixture.

Amniotic fluid (Tamil *panikkutanir*), the fluid in which floats the embryo and which comes out during parturition, has also been made part of muppu. Caught into vessels as it comes out, it was mixed with earth, or boiled, and the salt which such process produced has been designated as muppu to be ingested.[12]

Most frequently mentioned and, it would seem, textually documented, is the use of menstrual blood as muppu or part of it.[13] Some Siddha texts recommend, in fact, 'to lick the vagina of virgins (*kanniyin yoni*) and swallow the red liquid (*cikappu natam*) which appears there, as *kayacitti*'. There are three opinions about the well-known Siddha text which is given below in close and faithful translation: one is that it designates *kamappal*, lit. 'milk of passion', i.e. the exudation of moisture due to sexual excitement in the female (most probably). Another is that it designates *cironitam*, i.e. menstrual blood (very improbable). The third opinion, valid even among some Siddhas, says that this is all nonsense, and that the whole text is clear and simple *paribhasha* usage of intentional metaphorical language.[14]

> 'On the seventh day after periods have struck[15]
> approach the young women,[16] and getting hold
> of the cups of her breasts,
> make [her] lie down, after having consumed
> [some] betel-leaf.
> In front of the couch spread open the banana-leaves,[17] nose [and] ear outside,[18]

---

12 In the text called *Tanvantiri nikantu*, there are lines which could be taken as rationale for this identification.

13 One possible reason for such opinion maybe the fact that a metaphoric expression for menstruation (common in poetry, but also in day-to-day parlance) is *pu*, literally 'blossom, flower', or *puppu* 'flowering, blooming'. This usage is as ancient as the most ancient Tamil text preserved, Tolkappiyam Porulatikaram 187.

14 E.g. Vi. Palaramayya, Muppu kuru, Madras, 1971, 39.

15 Tamil original says, *takkuvatu rutuvana-y-ela(m)nalil.*

16 Technical term meaning literally 'juvenility'; the state of a young woman at or near puberrty.

17 Metaphoric expression for labia of the vulva.

[with] the tongue scoop the vulva of the bewitching damsel under her navel,
feel [it] with the fingers, [and] when, removing
the tongue,
you proceed to stroke the jewel,[19]
the milk of lust of the glowing woman will flow.'

Without getting into a particular discussion of this very outspoken and detailed instruction, I believe that this text, although belonging to the Siddha tradition (it is quoted even in a few contemporary Tamil sources), is either part of some erotic-sexological manual (the well-known *kamasastras*) or else it pertains to the Tantrik Siddha school.

Concluding the chapter on *kayakalpa* drugs we may mention two simple innocent items which according to the Siddhas should be in daily use as 'drugs' for longevity:

1. Lemon: anti-flatulent digestant, liver tonic, with mild antiseptic properties; high vitamin C content assures anti-inflammatory action; lemon pectin has good hemostatic effect. Even more important is

2. Garlic (Allium sativum) which is a liver stimulant, with proven anti-cholesterol and anti-rheumatic activity; anti-septic, anti-flatulent, digestant; very high bactericidal properties; anti-hypertensive. An old Siddha saying tells us that one should, in prevention and cure, use first leaves, stems and roots of herbs; if these are not effective, gradual use of metals and minerals is suggested.[20] One should of course always bear in mind that Siddha approach to healing, and even longevity, is 'holistic', that is to say that one should cure body and mind, one should rather prevent than cure and, also, that the method consists in skillful combination of the use of drugs as well as of applying Yoga exercises, controlled breathing, meditation and, in certain types of Siddha therapy, controlled use of sex.

---

18 This sounds funny ; but the meaning is, 'only with tongue outstretched so that other parts of the face (= nose-ear) remain outside.'

19 Current metaphor for clitoris.

20 Tam. *verparu talaiparu mincina-k kal / mella mella parpa centuram paru .*

11 Doctrines And Traditions Of The Siddhas

Siddha medical doctrines at present

According to R. Kumaraswamy,[1] there are fourteen basic points characteristic of contemporary Siddha medical doctrine:

1) Energy (*sakti*) manifesting as *uyir* or universal source of life: this doctrinal point derived from Tirumular's *Tirumantiram.*

2) The concept of *panca bhutam* or five cosmic elements as constituting the primordial matter.

3) Dual forces of creation (*vintu*) and destruction (*nacam*) controlling phenomena of life.

4) Concept of disease as energy crisis.

5) Use of mineral medicaments and cinnabar lingam.

6) Concept of ten energy currents (*tacanati*) in the body.

7) The science of *varmam.*

8) Pulse diagnosis as basis of medical diagnosis.

---

1 Prof. R.Kumaraswamy, of Palayamkottai, Tamilnadu.

9) Attempts at rejuvenation and the quest for immortality (*kalpacatanai*).

10) The art of moxa treatment (*muccukkalayam* practice).

11) The art of chiropractice (bone-setting).

12) Cult of *comavatam* (human elixir, *civampu*).

13) Urine therapy (*amuritaranai*).

14) Physiotherapy of skin and muscle through massage (*tokkanam*, also termed *tokkatam*).

1. Energy as universal source of life.

This concept derives from Tirumular's *Tirumantiram* which refers to the body as seat of universal energy and a 'temple of god', and hence must be fostered well to safeguard life (e. g. *Tirumantiram* 13:704).

The ultimate aim of the Siddhas has always been the art of rejuvenation and longevity for the sake of liberation. One of the means to rejuvenate the body is achieved through the art of breathing exercises which has direct bearing on basal metabolic rate, and hence on the span of life. This art is viewed as energy-conservation process (analogous to hibernation or aestivation of animals). Energy (Sanskrit *sakti*, Tam. *cakti, catti*) thus conserved and well used is the source of life in everything that lives, men, animals and plants.

2. The concept of panca bhutam.

Five cosmic elements constitute as primordial matter bodies of minerals, herbs, animals and humans. With this concept is closely connected

3. The view that all objects of phenomenal existence are either manifested or unmanifested phases of energy:

Men, animals and herbs are manifested phases of life-energy; metals and minerals are unmanifested phases of the same energy. The microcosm of human body is nothing but a miniature of macrocosm (cf. e.g. Cattaimuni, Nanam 33: *antattil ullate pintam*). The phenomenon of life is controlled by the dual forces of creation (*vintu*, literally sperm, semen virile; *vintunatam* male and female semen; union of male and female energies) and destruction (*nacam*). This theory of the five elements (earth, water, fire, wind, space) is ultimately derived from Samkhya philosophy and pervades the whole of Hinduism. When one dies, one 'returns 'to the five elements.

4. Concept of disease as the energy crisis in the human body.

Disease is basically disbalance between the positive (creative) and negative (destructive) flow of bioenergies. This is apparently in contrast to the concept of modern Western medicine which holds that pathology is physiology gone wrong (nowadays considered to be mostly conditioned by genetic programming).

After these more general tenets follow some more specific or concrete characteristics.

5. Use of minerals in medicine.

There are early textual data suggesting the use of arsenic and mercury in treating diseases. Mercuric sulphide in the form of cinnabar is praised as balancing positive and negative energies to such an extent that the divine blend of Siva-Sakti forces is said to exist in cinnabar itself. Hence it is called lingam. It is important to notice that lingam which elsewhere refers to either the phallus, or to the concretized symbol of male procreative force, or, in sublimation, to the principle and ultimate source of life, in Siddha texts may refer to the blend of sulphur and mercury in cinnabar used in medicine, and hence to the unity of Siva (male) and Sakti (female).

*6. Ten energy channels (*taca nati*).*

These exist in the body; they start from the finger and toe ends in pairs (genesis from digital tips). With this concept is closely connected

7. The praxis of varmam

(literally 'any vital part of the body') preserved mainly in the Kanyakumari district of Tamilnadu[2] which can be compared with Japanese acupressure and Chinese acupuncture methods. According to Dr. S. Rajamony (of Government Siddha medical college at Palayamkottai), the praxis has been applied with positive results in curing diseases of the nervous system including paralytic disorders, and also in some chronic diseases (arthritis, asthma, migraine, etc.).

8. Siddha science of pulse diagnosis.

Founded on principles of accoustics and resonance of musical instruments such as lute. This somewhat surprising statement derives

---

[2] The south western most tip of Tamil India.

from the concept of pulse which is different from the vascular pulse felt in the radial artery. According to the Siddhas, pulse is derived from omnipresent cosmic vibrations entering human body from the Universe and generating the energy required for the functioning of human metabolism.

9. Quest of immortality and science of rejuvenation

(discussed in some detail above).

10. The art of moxa treatment.

This practice seems to be South Indian in origin. In popularly applied form called *muccukkalayam* in Tamil, it used to be practised by old ladies as follows: A cotton wick soaked in the juice of *marukkoluntu* alias *maci-paccai* (Artemisia vulgaris) leaves was burnt slowly generating mild heat applied to nerve-endings at certain points of lumbar and abdominal regions, thus producing thermo-stimulus treatment. In the coded idiom of Tamil medicine this moxa weed (or 'mugweed') was called *kalacapuntu* ('cup-herb, pot-herb'). It is endemic in South Indian soil and climate, and used to be imported to China from India either by sea-routes or across the Himalayas.

11. The art of bone-setting or chiropractice.

I.e. practice of setting right fractures, sprains and dislocations of bones - in contrast to Western methods of maintaining immobility of the affected joints or bones.

12. Human Elixir.

According to the opinion of the Siddhas, during certain Yoga exercises, the midbrain (or, more precisely, the hypophalangeal region of midbrain containing the pineal body) secretes certain fluid designated as *civampu* (literally 'the flowering of *civam* ') described also as endogenous soma (as correlative to exogenous soma),[3] which has a

---

3 The exact nature of the exogenous soma is still a matter of uncertainty and dispute. G. Wasson (*Soma, the Sacred Mushroom*) in 1960 identified as the herbal source of soma juice the mushroom Amanita muscaria (Fly Agaric), endemic in Siberia, the Himalayan region, etc. This identification was questioned by others who tried to establish the source of soma as Himalayan ephedra, and generally by Indologists who are very sceptical about such identifications.

certain psychedelic spectrum of action since it contains components like serotonin and epinephrin.

13. Urine Therapy.

Urine (Tam. *amuri, muttiram, cirunir*) is described as ambrosia to prolong human life-span already as early as in Tirumantiram (probably ca. 550 A.D. or slightly later) which assigns separate chapter to it (Amuritaranai in the 3rd Tantiram). The scientific basis of urine therapy to fight disease and prolong life is the undisputed fact that fresh healthy urine in immediate use is asceptic and a bactericide.

14. Physiotherapy

Tokkanam (or *tokkatam*) is specific practice of skin and muscle massage. A cream known as *toyyil* (solution of sandalwood) used to be applied to the skin of female breasts and shoulders in a method known as 'toyyil writing'. Different types of cosmetic creams were used by the Tamils (*toyyil kulampu, cem-pancu kulampu* etc.) mentioned as early as ancient Tamil poetry of the so-called Sangam (Cankam, Academy, 3rd cent. BC. - 3rd cent. AD.). It is connected with painting the skin with herbal and other juices having medical (soothing, antiseptic) properties practiced universally by peoples in all continents, often as part of ritual. In Siddha medicine, such herbal and mineral unguents are used not only as skin and muscle tonics but also as treatment against herpes.

In addition, Siddhas believe in the healing and transformative power of sound produced by correct recitation and chanting of certain mantras (spells, formulae). That this is not to be regarded as 'false 'or 'empty'magic seems to be demonstrated by serious research performed by Jill Purce (who had been awarded Research Fellowship in King's College Biophysics Department, University of London, with Maurice Wilkins, Nobel prize for DNA research) who investigated spiritual dimensions of music and 'magical' properties of voice, and published many papers and articles and several books on the topic.[4]

In a Siddha Medical Dispensary

Let us enter together a small contemporary Siddha medical dispensary in Madras. The Siddha practitioner (called *vaittiya* or *vaittiyan* 'doctor/physician') has been trained within the gurukula system - that is,

4 Cf. her *The Mystic Spiral*, 1974.

he has gained his knowledge as family heritage in a succession from father to son (or, in direct transmission from master to student). His professional library is not rich: his books represent mostly palmleaf manuscripts and their printed versions (without commentaries which are offered orally), some of these regarded as indispensable: *Patarttakuna cintamani* (on materia medica, printed in 1931 but containing ancient material), Teraiyar yamaka venpa (1973, 1974), *Racavata cintamani*, *Vaittiya navanitam* in 10 parts, etc. In addition, there are a few books printed in English such as the *Formulary of Siddha Medicines* (Madras, 1972), *National Siddha Formulary* (Govt. of India, New Delhi, 1978) and *Siddha Hospital Pharmacopoeia* (Govt. of Tamilnadu, Madras, 1957). However, he will seldom consult these (if at all, as his knowledge of English is very limited).

Most of his medical knowledge is based on experience and stored in his memory. In common with most Siddha physicians, he has only a limited number of patients in his care, and hence the quantity of medicaments needed is also small. He prepares his own drugs, beginning with the collection of herbs and inorganic stuff, drying the herbs, processing the raw materials and, most important, making his own compositions. Another reason why he does not have a large number of drug preparations in his dispensary is his skill of controlling a variety of (seemingly) unrelated ailments by using a limited number of basic drugs with different supporting drugs (called *anupanam* or *tunai maruntu* in Tamil), many of these items being stuff which we would hardly call drugs (like ghee, honey, milk, various fruit and vegetable juices). The principle is most important: concurrent medication (or, supporting drug therapy; conjoint therapy) states that therapy becomes effective and complete only when a main drug is taken along with the prescribed *anupanam* (literally this word means 'with' + 'drink'). The term designates all liquid, semisolid and solid substances, administered before, along with, or after the main drug. This principle is stated clearly in the medical Siddha text *Teraiyar venpa* (446, 594 - 95). Stanza 446 states that efficacy of drugs is increased by supporting drugs (*anupanattale*); st. 594 also mentions some of these (*cukku* 'dry ginger' and *inci* 'fresh ginger', sugar-cane, water, cow's urine and milk, mother's milk - *mulaippal*, *ney* 'ghee', *ten* 'honey' and *verrilainir* 'betel juice'). St. 595 warns against non-specified and non-selective use of supporting drugs. J. Joseph Tas (Head, Dept. of Pharmacology, Govt. Siddha Medical College, Tirunelveli) gives the following instance of typical Siddha prescription according to the *anupana* principle. Basic drug: Kauri cintamani centuram (35 g of mercury + 35 g sulphur + 35 g borax). Grind mercury and sulphur into black mass, add borax, obtain homogenous mixture. Tie the product with a piece of cloth into small bundles of 1. 5 cm of diameter. Paste outside with clay. Place the bundles on layer of sand in an earthen disc. Cover with another sand-layer, cover with another disc, seal the rim. Burn capsule with ca. 100 cowdung cakes. Cool, open, collect packets. Finely grind and store the final black product. Dose: 65 - 130 mg for 40 days per day. Indications and *anupanam*: 1. Given with three-pungents-powder (1 part dry ginger + 1 part long pepper + 1 part dry pepper) in colic, bronchitis, piles, jaundice, rheumatism, inflammations and pains in genitalia, hepatitis, ulcers, eczemas, dyspnoea. 2. Given with nutmeg or cloves powder in stomach aches, diarrhoea and indigestion. 3. Given with bark of Tanner Cassia in diabetes. 4. Given with juice of Calotropis leaves induces purgation. Diet restrictions: Reduce salt to minimum. Only goat's milk may be drunk. Mutton may be eaten.

The above is a traditional prescription but, according to J. J. Tas, a contemporary publication, *Siddha Hospital Pharmacopoeia* (Uthamaroyan, 1957) devotes an entire chapter to *anupanam*. Such typical supporting drugs used in conjoint therapy are the above-mentioned *tirikatucuranam* (three-pungents-powder) used as a vehicle, or *tiripalacuranam* (chebulic myrobalan, belleric myrobalan and emblic myrobalan one part each) used for gargling and prepared as infusion.

5 A relatively recent and popular shrine of Valli alias Pongi alias Sri Vaisnavi is at Tirumullaivayil near Madras.

Let us return to our Siddha practitioner. Before he begins the examination he will perhaps shortly pray for guidance. The preferred goddess worshipped by those Siddhas who are not completely iconoclastic is Valai, a form of the Goddess (Isvari) or Bala, represented as a ten year old girl who stands for the quintessence of Sakti (Universal Energy) as knowledge.[5] Another manifestation of Sakti sometimes worshipped in the Madras area is Valli or Pongi who is supposed to confer on her devotees the eight siddhis or exceptional abilities.

After hearing out our symptoms the physician will examine our pulse (a most important part of the diagnostic procedure), perform perhaps yet other simple checks and tests (e.g. urine analysis), and then, if he is a good Siddha physician, follow the principle of 'maximum therapeutic efficacy with minimum toxicity'. He will prescribe the main drug with its *anupanam*, and then turn to dietary rules and possible restrictions. This part of the therapy is designated as *patyam*. Those items which are to be included in our dietary regimen are called *patya patarttas* or 'compatible substances' while those to be avoided are termed *apatya patarttas* or 'incompatible substances'.

According to the Siddhas, the difference between diet and drugs is not fundamental: taste is predominant in diet while potency is predominant in drugs. Food is drug and drug is food (cf. the Tamil Siddha saying *unavu maruntu marunte unavu*). Thus, in genuine Siddha medicine, the combination of drug - anupanam - patyam is a *sine qua non* of efficient therapy.

We proceed with our scrutiny of the Siddha dispensary. In a corner stand stone and metal mortars of different sizes, together with pestles, next to a fireplace with charcoal, with a mud crucible and a bower for blowing the fire. It looks a bit like a miniature alchemist's kitchen - and that's what it in fact is: for it is used to purify metals and some poisonous substances. Our question regarding purification processes is answered in the following manner: 'All the eight metals used in our practice will have impurities called *kalimpu*. Due to this stuff (which in the West is called verdigris on copper and rust on iron) the metals can be dangerous or even poisonous. This *kalimpu* should either be completely removed or converted, neutralized. The simplest method of purification is by

---

5 Cf. *Madurai Temple Art Museum Series*, 1965, 53. It is important to realize that Siddha physicians worship a *female* deity; the ideological basis of their worship is shaktic.

immersing the substances, for instance cinnabar, in breast-milk for three days. But there are stuffs which must be purified with fire. Take for instance *turucu* "copper sulphate".' And our Siddha goes on to describe the procedure in detail: 'Powder copper sulphate in this small mortar. Prepare a mixture of equal portions of ghee and pure honey. Put this mixture drop by drop on the copper sulphate and grind. When its consistency becomes waxy, stop. Fill a *kukai* (mud crucible) with the copper sulphate paste, cover. Place on charcoal fire. When the mixture becomes hard mass, take the crucible out, let it cool off. Then break it and take the sulphate mass out. Subsequently put a few drops of lime juice into a vessel with milk, and when a sediment develops, pour the whey water in another vessel and put the copper sulphate mass into it. Let it soak for three days. After three days, take it out and dry it in the sun. Copper sulphate thus purified is free from toxicity and can be used for preparation of medicines to be taken orally.'

The present author actually made use of such a Siddha dispensary in Madras out of necessity in January 1968, suffering from a stubborn dysentery condition which Western-type medicine refused for days to cure; he was directed to a Siddha physician who prescribed two kinds of remedy: [1] Powdered nutmeg taken with honey several times a day (called *jatikkay poti*), to relieve dysentery and act as an antispasmodic agent with sedative and even anti-inflammatory effects. But, more importantly [2] a powder called *tayircunti curanam*. This is a potent medicine of great value. The exact manner of preparation was not revealed but its main components were described as: powdered dry ginger (Zingiber officinale, *cukku*) which is added with four other salts to fermented curds (*tayir*) and dried completely in the sun to a solid mass, then powdered. Taken several times per day. The four salts are sodium chloride, sodium carbonate, potassium nitrate and soda bicarbonate.

Within a few days, the present author was cured. The swift effectiveness of the cure impressed me greatly, and my interest in Siddha medicine was thus substantially stimulated. A subject which until then I knew only from textual study, and which interested me mostly as relevant to certain school of medieval Tamil poetry, became in fact a matter of rather personal experience, and led not only to study in depth of Tamil Siddha matters, but also to personal participation in some Siddha observances, rites, etc. One of the results is the present book, written, as stated above, with sympathy and yet with critical scepticism.

12
Tantrik Siddhas and Siddha Attitudes to Sex

The Siddhas share some very general and all-embracing attitudes with Tantrism: with some (notable!) exceptions, the rejection of asceticism (the most notable exception being Pattinattar); decisive rejection of priestly hierarchy and dominant position of Brahmins, and of the caste system. However, in many other respects, the Tamil Siddhas come rather closely to standard Tamil Saivism: some among the greatest Siddha thinkers and poets tend towards the ascetic model of Siva who dances on the cremation ground. In general, meat-eating, wine-drinking and sexual license (typical features of classical Tantrism) are *not* encouraged by the Siddhas.

Nevertheless, there has been a not negligible branch of the Siddha movement which shares with Tantrism some important fundamental insights (e.g., the conviction that the world is not an illusion but real) and practices, in particular when it comes to the male-female sexual relationship.[1] The ideological basis of Tamil Tantrik-Siddha sexual ritualism is rooted in a fundamental binarism which views everything that exists in creation in terms of two contrastive but necessarily complementary entities: passive (Siva) and active (Sakti), positive and negative, light and dark, day and night, and, quite concretely, male and female. Sex is the expression of *cosmic* union of opposites (it is very important that this dual contrast is conceived of in terms of the cosmos, in universal terms!). During each cycle of Cosmic Inaction there exists but 'One'. This One (designated in Tamil Siddha parlance as *civam*-neuter gender - or, more abstractly, as Void) becomes two / many by an act of *will*. Civam becomes Siva (masculine) and Sakti (feminine). When a union of male and female occurs, the couple provide a field of cosmic force, apart from being a model, on the human plane, of the Siva-Sakti union. The psycho-sexual energy which is thus generated can even produce 'inexplicable' phenomena in many realms (psychical, mental, spiritual, physical). This is so because mind and matter are but two different modes of existence of the same ultimate power, one subtle (mind), the other gross (matter). The human partners become a divine couple since through them flows this cosmic, creative energy of the universe. The woman *is* thus Sakti or Parasakti ('Supreme Power') herself, and the man does not only represent but actually incarnates Siva. This is expressed neatly and forcefully in colour symbolism: the red colour of woman's menstrual blood (Tamil *[i]rattam, rajas, pon*, liter. 'gold')[2] is *the* colour of the Goddess, of Sakti; the white colour of man's sperm (Tam. *vintu, sukla, velli*, liter. 'silver')[3] is *the* colour of Siva. Hence also the red dot on female forehead (the *kunkuma pottu* made of turmeric with alum and lime juice), hence the stripes made with white sacred ash (*vibhuti, tiruniru*) on man's forehead and the symbol of three white stripes with central red dot signifying the union of both, adorning the forehead of Saiva and Tantrik devotees. Hence also the red and white

1 It is perhaps necessary to mention the fact that *any* form of homosexuality, male or female , is completely ignored and even rejected by this tradition; Tantrism and Siddhism are by their very nature strictly heterosexual.

2 Although in Hindu culture in general, menstrual blood is considered most polluting, in some 'extremist' groups of Tantrik Siddhism it is recommended that sexual union takes places precisely with a menstruating woman, so that the merging union is effected of *velli* 'silver', i. e. male seed, and *pon* 'gold', i. e. menstrual blood.

3 Cf. also ftn. 20 for terminology.

stripes designating the boundaries of sacred space, e.g. the fences and walls of South Indian shrines and temples.

On the following pages will be described in detail Siddha Tantrik sexual practice,[4] and a few words will be added about 'secular' sex in Siddha regimen.

Absolute Reality is non-dual (*a-dvaya*), that is, it contains all dualities and polarities. Creation, becoming, represents the destruction of this primordial Unity,[5] and the emergence and separation of two principles. Man, experiencing a state of duality, a state of contrasts and oppositions, suffers, since this experience is illusion, bondage, angst.[6] To destroy this illusion and be free of this suffering, one has to *realize* the unity, i.e. one has to *act*. And one mode of realization of the primordial unity, one kind of *action* is the *sexual act*. Hence, sexuality is ritual. The sexual act is 'sanctified' and homogenized with myth and ritual.

The concept of ritual sexuality is pan-Indian and very ancient, going as far back as the later Vedic era. Thus, e.g., the very old *Aitareya Brahmana* X. 3. 2-4 says, 'If, in the course of recitation, the priest separates the first two quarters of a verse and brings the other two close together, this is because the woman separates her thighs and the man presses them during pairing. The priest thus represents pairing, so that the sacrifice will give numerous progeny.'

A somewhat younger text, *Brhadaranyakopanisad* VI. 4. 3 says, while speaking of the female partner in the Tantrik ritual: 'Her lower part is the sacrificial altar; her hairs the sacrificial grass, her skin the soma-press. The two labia of the vulva are the fire in the middle. Verily, as great as is the world of him who performs the Vajapeya sacrifice, so great is the world of him who, knowing this, practices sexual intercourse; he turns the good deeds of the woman to himself; but he, who without knowing this, practices sexual intercourse, his good deeds women turn to themselves.'[7]

To quote the most prestigious Tamil source: Tirumular, in *Tirumantiram* 813, states briefly but clearly the basic properties of sexual

---

4 The information given here is based on published accounts, textual study, data offered by Tamil Siddhas, and some personal experience.

5 This is certainly not a specifically Siddha insight. It is not even a Tantrik or Hindu insight. Buddhism, in particular Mahayana, shares this view, too.

6 This, again, is a conclusion common to both Hinduism and Buddhism.

7 Trans. S. Radhakrishnan.

union as practiced in Tantrik Siddha tradition: 'The age reached [by the woman should be at least] twenty and [that of the man at least] thirty. The woman with rich tresses, and the splendid man, who are [sexually] united, experience highest bliss. The Mind has blossomed and spread and dissolved [in bliss] after [the man] attained union with the woman. But the semen will *not* trickle and wither.'

The final target of Tantrik Siddha ritual is the freedom from the misery of clinging and attachment. The Tantrik enstasy is reached through the immobilization of mind, breath , and the seminal fluid. Control of breath is the first (and in fact relatively easiest) step; control of seminal ejaculation during sexual union the next step; control of mind the final step. However, arresting breath, seminal emission, and discursive thinking should be performed simultaneously. The simultaneous control of breath and seminal emission while in sexual union with the Sakti is supposed to bring about the suspension of all discursive mental functions, and, at the same time, contribute to the Siddhas 'search for physical immortality'.[8]

How do the Tantrik Siddhas perform their ritual to achieve this?[9]

According to the Siddha tradition, Tantrik ritual copulation may be undertaken at any time which is convenient, although the late evening and early night are to be preferred. One of the most suitable times is the first day after the cessation of the female partner's menstruation. This is, however, not obligatory. If performed by more persons than one couple, a circle (*cakkiram*) of male and female participants is formed so that each male has his partner on his left side, and the circle is presided by a senior Siddha. However, I shall describe the ritual *as if* performed by one couple of Siddha Tantrik participants only. In whatever follows the reader should always bear in mind that 'the postulated target is never to

---

8 Serious students of Indian Tantrik tradition should consult the essential book on this topic, Agehananda Bharati's *The Tantric Tradition* (1st ed. 1965, 3rd impression 1970), Rider, London. See also his *Great Tradition and Little Traditions:Indological Investigations in Cultural Anthropology*, Varanasi, 1978.

9 Since the information that follows is rather difficult to obtain, and since a lot of nonsense has been said and written about it by 'guffawing occidentals' (A. Bharati) who charge that Tantriks pretend to be religious in order to indulge in drink and fornication, the whole ritual will be described in great and *authentic* detail.

be sought in the enjoyment of the used materials; it is not an any time a hedonistic motive that directs the ritualistic acts' (A. Bharati). This is equally true of the meat, fish, parched cereals, liquor, as well as sexual union. The liquor, called *amutam* 'nectar', is identified with the menstrual flow of the Goddess.[10]

The ritual, as known in Tantrik Siddha tradition, is very carefully structured,[11] and may be thought of as consisting of three main parts: a preparatory part, preliminary disciplines, and ritual coitus proper.

Preparatory part.

Ritually, this slot of the whole event is considered a purification of the *tattvas*, i.e. ritualistic purification of body organs. Siva and Sakti are invoked with various magic formulae to purify the gross and the subtle body. In practice this means that both partners bathe carefully from head to toe, dress, and put on scents.

The female partner (henceforth termed sakti)[12] will use scents in abundance. This has several reasons. Nature tells us that essential ingredients of most perfumes are related to sexual functions of plants and animals (e. g. musk is obtained from a gland of the male musk deer used as a sex lure).[13]

---

[10] In practice, this can be any alcoholic beverage, e.g. fermented honey, local or imported wine, or even beer.

[11] It is possible that the fundamental elements of this structured Tantrik Siddha ritual could be culled from an early and highly important work in Tamil, viz. *Tirumantiram* by Tirumular (perhaps 6th c. A.D.). This difficult text of some 3000 stanzas will have to be studied very carefully. So far it has not been the case, although lately partial and full translations into English have appeared in India.

[12] Here one word on the choice of the female partner: She must be of good health, with a body free of physical defects, fully developed breasts, prominent *alkul* (mons veneris) and abundant hair (on the head; pubic hair, on the contrary, is most often shaved off). However, her age and social group (caste) is of no importance whatsoever ; the sakti can be a girl of 16 or a lady of 60; she can be a Brahmin or a Harijan ('Untouchable'). In fact, a verse in *Mahanirvanatantra* warns against caste-distinctions in Tantrik ritual (8th *ullasa*) !

[13] History is replete with instances of aphrodisiac properties of scent: Cleopatra and Caesar, Empress Josephine and Emperor Napoleon III are telling examples. It is also reported that Henri IV (1553 -1610) became infatuated

Different scents are used in Tantrik sex-rites in a strictly prescribed order for different parts of the female body: oil of jasmine is used for palms of hands; patchouli (Indian marjoram, Pogostemon spp.) for cheeks and breasts; spikenard for the hair, sandalwood powder for inner sides of thighs, saffron powder for feet, and musk (kasturi), the strongest of perfumes, for mons veneris (*alkul*). The main reason for using scent in Tantrik ritual is stimualtion of the root-center (*mula -taram*); a secondary reason is general sexual stimulation; there is also the hygienic and aesthetic component which accompanies the use of scents.

The root-center (*mulataram* < Sanskrit *muladhara-*) situated midway between anus and genitals is of utmost importance in Tantrik ritual; it is imagined as a triangle inside which is a brilliant red tongue of flame. After bath, the sakti dons always a red garment, and the partners enter together the ritual chamber. However, in some traditions, the male partner enters alone and will partake of the wine, meat, fish and parched grain alone, after he had first performed certain Yogic breathing exercises. The sakti (who had eaten and drunk separately) is only then called in, consecrated, bathed, dressed in her red robe, and made to sit down on the couch.

We shall, however, proceed in our description as if both partners entered together (which is the custom in South Indian Tantrik Siddha ritual).

The essential component of the preparatory part is the male partner's breath control and sexual self-stimulation. The breath-control corresponds basically to Yogic breathing exercises including retention of breath; during the period of retention (holding the breath), the man should focus his awareness on the base-center of the Yogic body and perform mental worship of the basic Sakti there whose aspect is the force which is coiled up on that spot. At the same time, he should stimulate the center by contracting the muscles of the anal sphincter, visualizing the union of Siva and Sakti. He should also mentally inject the image of the Sakti on the couch. This stimulation of the root-center is repeated twelve times, whereupon the male worships the couch. Thereby the preparatory part is over, and preliminary disciplines may begin.

---

with Gabrielle d'Estrees (d. 1599) at the moment when she handed him her musk-saturated handkerchief to wipe his brow during a dance.

Preliminary disciplines.

Both partners participate, whether or not the sakti has been present thus far.

1. *First 'worship' of the female partner as Sakti*: The male touches her forehead, eyes, nostrils, lips, arms and thighs with his right hand (while pronouncing certain formulae). Then he feeds her areca-nut in betel-leaf (Tamil *verrilaippakku*), and touches lightly her pudenda (while muttering certain magic syllables).

2. *Pancikaranam.* This consists, roughly speaking, of preparation for the ritual eating and drinking of the 'five M's' of meat (*mamicam* < Sanskrit *mamsa-*), fish (*maccam* < *matsya-*), parched grain or kidney bean (*muttirai* < *mudra-*) and liquor (*mattiyam* < *madya-*). It is a kind of consecration of the food to be eaten and the liquor to be drunk, with certain prescribed sacred mantras. The actual consumation of the ingredients is accompanied by silent *japa* (repetition) of various benedictory and magic mantras and by meditation. Also, certain ritualistic etiquette is to be followed.[14]

3. *Partaking of the food and drink.* The general procedure consists of consuming the food followed by the liquor followed by consuming the food followed again by drinking, etc., in alternation. Small cups are filled about two-thirds full with the liquor. Then, meat is eaten from a *patra* (bowl); the meat (usually goat or sheep, never beef or pork) cut in small pieces is held between the thumb and the third finger of the right hand. Only one piece of meat is consumed by each participant at a time. After another dosis of the beverage, a small portion of the fish is eaten. Then again, wine is drunk. Thereafter, parched grains are consumed: this is often parched kidney bean or some cereal (prepared in a manner which is thought to be aphrodisiacal, e.g. with asafoetida[15]). In our times, these can even be specially prepared biscuits (!). Once more the cups are emptied and refilled. After the final drink, the cups are filled with clean

---

[14] Thus one should take the food and the liquor silently; one should not spill even a drop of the beverage; one should sip the liquor, not empty it in one go; etc.

[15] Hindi *hing*, Tamil *perunkayam*, which is used in Ayurvedic and Siddha medicine against impotence, brown resinous substance with strong smell obtained from roots of some plants.

cool water, used to rinse the mouth. In South India, cardamom[16] is then consumed. The participants break open the husk, for a while meditate on the shape of the grains, and then chew them 'to sweeten their breath.'

4. *Second 'worship' of the female partner*. The partners proceed to the consecrated couch. The sakti takes off her clothes (except for the jewelry) and seats herself so that she spreads her legs widely apart. The male partner contemplates her beauty and the mysteries of creation and procreation. Without the contemplation of the sakti as divine energy and potential mother of creation, the sexual intercourse which follows would be a hedonistic, carnal act. The naked woman incarnates nature and is transformed into Sakti, the Goddess; the male incarnates Siva. Their ritual copulation *is* the copulation of the divine couple.

The simultaneous arresting of the flow of semen, the immobilization of respiration, and the suspension of thought are destined to conquer our 'being in time', our 'historicity', to transcend the human condition.

The actual second worship of the sakti is performed so that the man places the tips of his fingers on certain parts of the female body, uttering the appropriate mantras. This is called *niyacam*, lit. 'putting down, placing, inserting'.[17] With the index and middle fingers of the right hand, the man touches lightly and precisely the woman's crown of the head (or her forehead), eyes (or the two eyelids and the center of her forehead), the hollow of her throat (or nostrils), left and right earlobes (or lips), breasts, upper arms, navel, thighs, knees, feet, and vulva.[18]

5. *Preparation for coitus*. The male now removes his own robe, and the partners lie together on the couch: the woman on the left side of the

---

[16] Elettaria cardamomum, Tamil *elam*, Sanskrit *ela-* (derived from Dravidian, cf. Dravidian Etymological Dictionary R 907). The purple-blackish seeds (in light-coloured outer husk) are bivalvular (the two halves form a unity within the enfolding sheath), like all creation which appears to be dual but is in fact a unity.

[17] Sanskrit *nyasa-*; defined as assignment of various parts of the body to different deities with appropriate mantras. However, in Siddha Tantrik Yoga it also wakes up vital forces which lie dormant in these various parts of the body.

[18] I also received some information to the effect that the vulva is being kissed by the 'chief' Siddha when the sakti as a chosen representant of the Goddess is sitting in the middle of the circle of participants. This information should probably be taken with certain reserve. As A. Bharati (*op. cit.* p. 264) writes, 'osculation [is] no part of the Hindu tantric practice proper'.

male, and reclining on her back, while he lies upon his left side facing her. The sakti will raise both legs by bending her knees and pulling them towards her chest. The male brings his phallus into close contact with her vulva. She lowers her legs and he places his right leg between her legs. The sexual organs are thus brought close together, but insertion has not yet taken place.

Ritual coitus (Tamil punarcci; maittunam < maithuna-).

Fully relaxed, the male should gently part the labia of the vulva with his hand or lips, and *partially* insert the penis. Deep penetration of the vagina is at this moment not desirable. The partners should remain motionless and relaxed, visualizing the flow of *prana* (vital air) between them, in particular between their sexual organs. The sensual pleasure producing maximum tension abolishes normal consciousness. Orgastic contraction of the body's muscles follows, and a state which is termed *camaracam* (Sanskrit *samarasa-*), liter. 'equality, harmony, identity' (Tamil *orrumai*) follows, based on simultaneous arrest of breath, thought and sperm. A moot question arises: Can the sperm be finally ejected or should it remain retained? According to A. Bharati (*op. cit.* p. 265), the main difference 'between the Hindu and the Buddhist tantric *sadhana* seems to have been that the Hindu tantric ejects his sperm, the Buddhist Vajrayana adept does not.' Bharati even writes (*ibid.*) that the male participant 'in the end,... abandons his sperm (*sukra tyag kare*)...'; and he quotes the *Hevajra Tantra* which does not indicate the necessity of retaining the semen.

However, in South Indian Siddha Tantrik tradition, ejaculation should not at all occur. Stabilizing the three items, breath, thought, and semen by arresting them in a simultaneous act brings about intensely euphoric (perhaps psychopathological) feeling which yields the state of oneness in the duality of the two participants. The release of semen is also discouraged because *coitus reservatus* (retention of semen) is a form of birth control. It is said that the bliss of retaining and rechanneling the semen (reversing its flow back into the body) is much greater than ejaculating. In contrast, ejaculation is supposed to negate the rite, and could lead to insanity and even death (!). Since semen is the physical manifestation of Siva, it is not to be squandered. It is rather to be concentrated in the male during the sex ritual and directed through the 'conduits' (*nadis*) to the crown of the head, where the ultimate unity with the Absolute Void is achieved.

My Siddha informant even told me how to perform the arresting of the semen. If, during the coitus, the male feels that ejaculation will be imminent, he should seize his penis with the middle fingers of the left hand at its root in front of the anus and pressing hard, expel slowly his breath through the nose, at the same time performing contractions of anal muscles, drawing them inward and upward.[19] If emission does occur, the whole ritual is terminated. If the male is successful in arresting the flow of the sperm, he may continue to maintain the coital position for some time (even for several hours if the participants so desire).

The whole ritual may then be terminated so that the couple slides into slumber or, according to some traditions, the male will end with the emission of the semen which is then abandoned as libation on the sacrificial altar - that is, in the yoni (vulva) of the sakti who embodies the Goddess.

'Secular' sex in Siddha tradition.

It has been said above that the Siddha attitude toward sex is ambiguous. On the one hand, there is a strong ascetic trend in Siddhism which is in direct contrast to the Tantrik Siddha tradition just described. On the other hand, there is a minor but very important branch of the Siddha school which adopts almost without alteration Tantrik insights and practices. On the whole, however, the overall attitude of contemporary Siddha practitioners towards sex is very similar to that which one can recognize in the most authentic and prestigious ancient poet of the tradition, Tirumular.

---

19 *Asvinimudra* or *mulabandha*: anal sphincters are forcibly contracted, the abdomen pulled in simultaneously, chin pressed against the chest, diaphragm pushed up towards the thorax. Another method is simply holding one's breath and turning one's tongue backward as far as one can against the roof of the mouth, with simultaneous contraction of anal sphincter. - Omar Garrison (1964, reprint 1973) tells of a Tantrik master who was conducting 'a kind of night school' in Brindaban and who arranged a ritual circle with women for final initiation. One of the students 'did not restrain his bindu... Instead, he is spending his seed, like one devoid of all dharma... Even a worse thing. To the others of the circle, he is saying , "This is very jolly. Let us indulge." Is there need for saying more? They all were discharging with shouts like players at a polo match or a gymkhana. So the fruit of their long *sadhana* was lost. It is still lost.'

In his sex life, the practitioner is encouraged to make an uninhibited response to bodily demands, in order to sublimate them into spiritual ecstasy. It would indeed be odd if the Siddha tradition which takes care of one's body with such profound interest and meticulous attention did ignore sexual activity.

Some of the Siddha manuals composed in Tamil (even quite recently) offer elaborate instructions for men about the techniques used to satisfy women in sexual encounter. According to an illustrated manual published in 1956 in Mysore, there exists an unfailing technique which consists of four phases: Phase 1: when the sex play reaches its summit, it is advisable to stroke and kiss the woman's nipples (Tamil *kampu*). Phase 2: next, one should kiss gently but persistently her clitoris (in Siddha Tamil texts described as *yoniyil irukkum paruppupponra pakam* 'the pea-like bit in the vulva'). Phase 3: Then it is advisable to stroke and knead firmly the whole surface of the vulva with bent ring-finger and little finger while the index and middle fingers are inserted gently inside. Phase 4: when her orgasm approaches, one should suddenly withdraw the hand and insert vigorously one's erect penis.

Siddha texts maintain unanimously that there is a female flow (*tiravam* 'liquid, juice') which corresponds to male semen (*vintu*). Moreover, they recommend the fresh mixture of male sperm and this female pre-orgasmic and orgasmic flow as beneficial for potency and general health when swallowed immediately after coitus. Special pills are prepared from male sperm and female discharge (or even menstrual blood!) to heal certain types of mental (!) illness. Sperm,[20] when

[20] Terminology: Semen virile: *velli*, literally 'silver; whiteness; Friday'; *pintu*, *vintu* (< Sanskrit. *bindu-*); *cukkilam* (< Sanskrit. *sukla-*) 'whiteness, paleness' (*cukkilakalitam* 'seminal discharge', *cukkilattampam* 'art of restraining the semen'); male seed is connected with the Moon (*candra-*). Semen muliebre, ovum, germ cell: *natam*; female sex-fluid: *tiravam*; menstrual blood: *cironitam, conitam*; *rajas* (connected with the Sun, *ravi-*); penis: *kulal* (lit. 'pipe, tube, flute'); *linkam* (< Sanskrit. *linga-*), *cicinam* (< Sanskrit. *sisna*); female sex-organ: *yoni*; vagina, vulva: *yonittuvaram* (< Sanskrit. *yonidvara-* lit. 'the door to yoni'); *yonivay* (lit. 'mouth of yoni'); clitoris: *yonimani* (lit. 'yoni-jewel'), also *yonilinkam*; *alkul*: general Tamil term for region below female waist; female sex-organ in general; specifically Venus' mound. *Natakkulal* (or *vintukkulal*) 'Fallopian tubes'; *natakkumil* 'Graafian vesicles'; *natacayam* 'ovary'. There are of course many metaphoric expressions pertaining to sex-organs and activities, *kuli* (lit., 'pit, hole, hollow') for

swallowed mixed with ground pepper, is supposed to be of great regenerative and rejuvenating power.

Although cunnilingus and fellatio (oral-genital sex) are usually discouraged and even abhorred in classical Hindu erotological texts (the classical *kamasastras*), in Tantrik Siddha tradition (at least in South India) genital kisses and oral-genital sex are highly recommended. Great role is attributed to pheromones, sex odours which affect males and females (women are said to be more susceptible). The clean genital odour of both sexes is considered to be an inbuilt stimulus.

Among common aphrodisiacs the texts mention garlic, onion, asafoetida, coriander seeds, pepper and ginger. For the benefit of those readers who may be surprised or even shocked by some aspects of Siddha Tantrik ideas and practices, and by the fact of seeming inconsistency and ambivalence of the Siddha attitudes to sex, I may quote Agehananda Bharati (alias Leopold Fischer) who writes: 'Thanks to the perseverance of Hindu philistine medievalism, to Christianity, to Gandhism, and to the puritanism of an inceptive industrial India, *the infinitely delicate and profound balance between celibacy and erotocentric ritualism has been lost* in a welter of narrow-minded, collectivizing religious observances which are Hindu only in name '(italics mine, KVZ).[21] This is precisely how a Siddha would feel and formulate it. When coming to terms with the Tantrik tradition we must not for a moment forget that the female partner, the sakti, stands for the dynamic, active principle in the cosmos, while the man represents the still, endless, contemplative element, Siva. When he and his female partner unite, they represent Siva and the Goddess in their eternal union, and only this union is the true ground of all Being, is the totality and unity of the universe. As for them themselves, they seek perfection and liberation, final emancipation through orgasmic bliss; their sexual ecstasy is a door to spiritual experience.

Many Western-educated modern Hindus share with most Westerners their shock and abhorrance of Tantrik tradition. They are (to employ the characteristics provided by Agehananda Bharati) filled with a 'unique mixture of sentimental cultural chauvinism, the idea that what is old in

---

vagina, *kumil* (lit. 'bubble, knob, stud') for clitoris, *kamanir* (lit. 'lust-water') for female sex-flow, *alkulil karikara lilai* (lit. 'karikkara-play in the *alkul*') for simultaneous stimulation of the vulva with tongue and fingers, etc.

21 *The Ochre Robe: An Autobiography*. Doubleday ed. 1970, p. 99.

religion is better, that everything Indian is the oldest and therefore best, that all religions mean essentially the same namely "be good" and "trust God", that the East is utterly spiritual, the West utterly materialistic' - a mixture which he calls 'pious trash... more nauseating... than outright pornography'. He quotes a Hindu sage, Mandalesvar, as saying, 'If God does not mind creating a human or an animal penis or a human and an animal vagina, and if he does not mind arranging a particular relation between their carriers, why should He hesitate to talk about them? Who are we to tell Him what is decent and what ought to be said... The relation between woman and man should be looked upon as an aspect of the divine, "not as a work of the devil"'.[22] This is precisely how the Siddha tradition in general and Siddha Tantrik tradition in particular regard sex.

மின்போலத் தோன்றி விடுமுலக வாழ்வனைத்தும்
என்போலி கள்திரமென் றெண்ணுவார்;—தன் போகம்
இல்லார் சிவபோக மென்றும் அருந்தியிடும்
நல்லார் திரமிதுவென் னார்.

தேசமூர் பேர்காணி சீர்வரிசை சாதியெனும்
ஆசையால் நெஞ்சே! அலையாதே—நேசப்
பொருப்பானை நின்னறிவிற் போக்கு வரவற்
றிருப்பானைப் பார்த்தே யிரு.

6. Specimen of modern printed edition of Siddha texts: Civapokacaram, with contemporary illustration of Meditating Siva.

[22] Ibid. 137.

13 Conclusions

The search for alternative systems of medicine - that is, alternative to the generally accepted Western-oriented modern medical science - has been going on for some time in America and Europe, and seems to be at present very much in vogue. To this author, 'alternative' in this context does not mean 'preferable', but 'additional' or 'supplementary'. No sane person anywhere would deny the tremendous achievements of modern medical science, particularly in such fields as surgery, cardiology, neurology, genetics, radiology, eradication and prevention of dangerous and epidemic infectious diseases etc. However, other cultures than ours, which is based on Judaeo-Graeco-Roman-Christian heritage, have established, too, their systems of healing, and it would be foolish to ignore them. Some of these systems have already partly entered the West with considerable success as, precisely, supplementary therapies (e.g. acupuncture or acupressure).

Out of the three main systems of Indian medicine, two indigenous - Ayurvedic and Siddha - and one imported - Yunani - the Siddha is the least known and the least exploited. The Hindu Ayurveda and the Perso-Islamic Yunani are still very active. 'Both these systems, though based in their classical forms on false premises, are pragmatically effective in curing and relieving many diseases, and their drugs and therapy are less expensive than those of modern Western medicine. Thus *ayurveda* in India and *yunani* medicine in both India and Pakistan still have an important part to play in maintaining the health of the people, especially of the poorer people.'[1]

Evaluating critically Siddhism, that is the Siddha movement in all its aspects, we should distinguish among at least three components which, though closely and intimately connected, can be discussed separately : Siddha philosophical basis; Siddha medicine as applied healing system; and Siddha quest for 'immortality'.

One may perhaps legitimately ask whether the Siddha tradition is part and parcel of orthodox Hindu tradition, or whether the Siddhas stand so to say apart, outside of it. The Hindu tradition insists on only very few axioms: first, that the Veda (in the broad sense) is revealed (technical term is *sruti*, literally 'hearing; that which is heard'), not 'man-made'; second, that there is rebirth; third, that there is an absolute spirit which is both immanent (= *atman*) and transcendent (=*brahman*). If this is so, then the Siddhas are, more or less, within the Hindu orthodoxy, but indeed on its fringes, since some among them, albeit carefully and with hesitation, question the second axiom.[2]

The achievements of Siddha healing praxis, of the Siddha system of medicine, cannot be denied. Although some of the basic axioms of Siddhism *seem* to be false, and some of the methods appear to be bizarre, odd, or outright nonsensical,[3] the results have proven to be effective in actually curing or at least relieving a number of diseases. Some of the premises, though, are attractive and may in future be proven correct. The Siddha advances from rational, discursive observation to intuitive, non-discursive thought. One of his basic premises is the interconnectedness

---

1 A.L.Basham, 'Conclusion', in *A Cultural History of India*, Oxford, 1975, 493. It is significant, that the other Hindu system of medicine, that of the Siddhas, is not even mentioned by Basham.

2 Compare this position with the Buddhist stand: for the Buddhist, the Veda is certainly not a revealed authority, and, above all, there is no absolute permanent spirit which would be both immanent and transcendental (the anatta doctrine). However, the Buddha has adopted a kind of rebirth into his doctrine. The basic elements of the Buddhist view can be formulated as follows: quest of enlightenment (bodhi); life is impermanent, imperfect, and selfless; the overcoming of craving (lust), aversion (hatred), and delusion; emphasis on deep insight (wisdom) and compassion; in contrast to revelation, personal experience.

3 Such as sympathetic magic (e.g. causing rain by pouring water) or adoptive magic (such as eating the tiger's heart to become brave).

of all phenomena; he views, intuitively, the patient as a body-mind entity within the context of universal, 'cosmic' forces. And although this may sound unusual, modern research in physics and biology seems to be in striking agreement with the insights of the Siddhas which are also, in yet somewhat other form, the insights of such Buddhist texts as the Avatamsaka sutra, and its follow-up in Hua Yen philosophy of China.[4] The experimental verification of Best's Theorem in 1982 at a Paris laboratory proves that everything from the largest star to the smallest photon is interconnected in a most intimate and immediate manner.[5] The new vision of reality, so similar to the insights of Hua Yen philosophy, and to some extent similar to the views of the Siddhas, is 'based on awareness of the essential interrelatedness and interdependence of all phenomena - physical, biological, psychological, social, and cultural.'[6] The nonlinear interconnectedness of living organisms indicates that the conventional attempts of biomedical science to associate diseases with single causes are highly problematic.[7] According to this 'new vision of reality' as well as according to the vision and approach of the Siddhas, the boundaries between an organism and the surrounding environment are difficult to ascertain.

Basically, the Siddha approach is holistic in more than one sense. First of all, for the Siddhas, body and mind form a unified field. A living organism is one ordered system in which physical and mental components form an interrelated, interconnected whole. Second, they believe that human beings as such are an integral part of an ordered larger system. And, third, that illness is the consequence of some disharmony in the human system. In close similarity with ancient Chinese medicine, the main themes of the Siddha approach to health and illness are: health as a state of balance, the importance of environmental influences, the interdependence of body and mind, and nature's inherent

---

4 At least two excellent publications on Hua-Yen philosophy to be recommended to the interested reader: Francis H. Cook, *Hua-yen Buddhism. The Jewel Net of Indra*. The Pennsylvania State University Press, 2nd printing, 1981; Thomas Cleary, *Entry into the Inconceivable. An Introduction to Hua-Yen Buddhism*. University of Hawaii Press, 1983.

5 Fritjof Capra, *The Turning Point*, Bantam ed., 1983, 265.

6 Best, Charles Herbert, Canadian physiologist (1899) of American origin. Discovered, with Sir F.G.Banting, insulin (1929).

7 Ibid. 269.

healing power.[8] Another point of agreement between Tamil Siddhas and ancient Chinese tradition was the concept of dynamic balance between two opposites: male:female, Siva:Sakti (Siddhas) and ying:yang (China). Both traditions believed that the human body-mind is a microcosm of the universe. Finally, we must not forget another striking tenet common to both Chinese and Siddha traditions: there exists a vital 'breath' or energy which animates the cosmos including its flow in human organism: *ch'i* in China, *prana* in India. And both traditions believed that disease becomes manifest due to causes leading to disharmony and imbalance, when the cosmic force does not circulate properly.[9]

The view of human organism as a living system whose components are all interconnected and interdependent, a living system which forms integral part of yet larger systems (natural environment, social contexts, cultural contexts) - that view together with more attention to intuition and a generally holistic attitude toward patients could no doubt enrich Western systems of medicine both in theory and practice. On a more concrete and less lofty level, some Siddha therapies are indeed worth while looking into critically yet sympathetically.

There are yet several other points to be mentioned here. First of all, it is perhaps necessary to stress that the exceptional 'magic' powers (siddhis) which almost all Siddhas claim to have achieved and mastered are not an irruption from the 'transcendental' into the 'mundane' but, on the contrary, an extension of the 'mundane', in other words, they are not 'miracles', but products of the Siddhas' discipline, of a strict, even tortuous regime. However, one should also keep in mind that when it is said that what has been achieved, is, e.g., the mastery of the body which can travel through air, passing unobstructed through walls, touching sun and moon, etc., what is meant is not the material body, the body of 'gross' matter, but a mind-made or mind-formed (*manomaya*) body which is produced from the physical body like 'a sword from the sheath, pith from a reed, a snake from a basket.' So much for the siddhis.

Another puzzling matter is the dual and controversial Siddha attitude toward sex. Hatred of women, disgust with the female body,

8 Cf. ibid. 312.

9 No wonder that some vague yet persistent traditions connect some Siddhas (notably Pokar - Bhoga) with China, either as being originally Chinese, or vice versa, Indians who went to China and therefrom brought back some elements of their doctrines.

abhorrence of sex on the one hand, so forcefully expressed in a number of Siddha poems - and, on the other hand, Tantrik Siddha rites of sexual congress, as well as open recommendations of medieval and modern Siddha medicine to indulge (within the boundaries of reason) in healthy heterosexual activity beneficial to the mind-body system of every individual, male or female. And yet, both tendencies, apparently so antagonistic, are found within the context of one movement, one tradition. Can this be satisfactorily explained, and can these two tendencies be reconciled within one ideology?

Perhaps a revealing analogy can be found in Buddhism. One Buddhist tradition regards sex as 'thirst' which creates the unease and suffering plaguing humanity. Women are 'nothing more than bags of skin filled with blood, pus, and filth', says Buddha to Mara's daughters sent to tempt him.[10] 'Do not cling to the body, a bag of bones plastered with flesh and blood.'[11]

And the Jatakas tell the following story which could be, just as it is, part and parcel of the ascetic stream of Siddha tradition.

An ascetic acquired a son in a most unusual manner: While bathing in a stream he emitted some semen into the water. The semen mixed with the water was swallowed by a doe, who miraculously conceived. The resultant boy-child was raised by the ascetic in the mountains and grew up unaware that females existed. To make a long story short, a girl from the city was sent to seduce the boy. After the boy innocently invited her into the hermitage, the girl showed him her 'wound.' 'A wild animal clawed off my organ,' she explained. 'The wound is very deep and itches terribly. If you want to help me, I'll show you the best way to scratch it.' When the boy's father returned just after the girl had departed, he asked why none of the chores had been done. 'Another boy, with the most unusual body, visited me. He taught me how to play doctor and other games. I enjoyed myself so much I forgot all about my duties.' The father explained the facts of life to the boy and made him promise never to do that again, for sex is anathema to an ascetic.[12]

---

10 N. Poppe, *Twelve Deeds of Buddha*, Wiesbaden, 1967, 122. This sounds almost exactly like the words of a Civavakkiyar or Pattinattar.

11 F.W. Burlingame, *Buddhist Legends*, London, 1962, vol.2, 336 ff.

12 John Stevens, *Lust for Englightenment. Buddhism and Sex*. Boston and London, 1990, 28-29 (based on Jatakas 523 and 526).

This, then, is the overall tone which one hears ringing loudly throughout the entire school of the puritan elders, and it is to be heard to this day in some Theravada countries as well as in certain neo-Buddhist movements in the West. 'It is better that your penis enter the mouth of a hideous cobra or a pit of blazing coals than enter a woman's vagina', the Buddha is reported to have said.

As against this, we have the whole powerful tradition of the Tantrik schools of Buddhism, well expressed in the message of the Tachikawa-Ryu, a medieval school of Japanese Tantra: 'The natural coupling of male and female is an adornment of Buddhahood. Sexual intercourse is the highest, not the lowest, form of human activity. It is the source of all religion and all that is best and most beautiful in human culture.'[13]

Thus, the movement of the puritan elders and the Tantrik schools seem to be in absolute mutual antagonism, and yet both are, indeed, genuine Buddhism. How can they be reconciled? How can the two contrasting attitudes between the two streams of the Siddha tradition be reconciled?

I believe that there is a twofold answer to this. First, it is the motive and not the act itself which is regarded as ethical, in agreement with the general Buddhist principle that it is the volition, the volitional decision, the motivation that decides what is kusala, i.e. skillful ('good') and what is akusala, i.e. un-skillful ('bad'). Also, as Stevens says, 'In sharp contrast to Judaism, Christianity, and Islam, in which sexual relations are regulated in detail, Buddhist moralists focused on the essentials.'[14] Hindu India has dealt in detail with the techniques of sexual relations, not with the moral and social issues connected with sex. Siddha Tantrik schools deal with the minutiae of ritual sex, with the ritualistic details to be observed in the sexual encounter of Tantrik adepts. So does Tantrik Buddhism. Why? Because - and this may be the second part of the answer to the question posited above - sexual passion is not an end in itself but the means to an end; it is a welcome tool for attaining enlightenment and liberation. In both traditions, the Hindu Siddha tradition as well as in the Buddhist tradition, the passions of sex are not

---

13 Ibid. p.80.
14 Ibid. p.140.

being denied[15] but transformed, transmuted into ultimate deliverance. Just as one must first develop one's ego into a strong self to ultimately rid oneself of that self in the true Self, so one must first experience the entire gamut of sexual passions to extinguish them and be totally free.[16]

Enough has been said about the quest of immortality of one's body in the introductory chapters. There can be no doubt that for many Siddhas (including relatively recent cases like that of Ramalinga in 1874) the belief in its possibility and even the conviction that they have achieved what they had set out to search for was very real. For others, 'immortality' became to mean, rather, 'eternal' youth, read 'greatly prolonged youth', health, and longevity. This led to the development of a discipline which would result in such achievements, and besides yoga and meditation, medicine and specific healing system became integral and very important parts of such sadhana. The ultimate aim, though, has always been and remained liberation, freedom, escape from the unease and ill of the human condition and the thraldom of mortal flesh, into the emancipation and liberty of an accomplished and perfected being, a true Siddha.

---

15 Cf. the words of Jiun, a monk who was a master of both Shingon and Zen Buddhism: '...It is foolish to say that passion is "nothing". Passion is a useful tool for attaining enlightenment' (in Stevens, *op.cit.* p.140).

16 This is in fact exatly what the Buddha went through after he had transcended both sexual indulgence as well as ascetic abstinence. 'Detachment can only come after attachment. By passion the world is bound, and by passion it is released.'

14
Siddha Poetry And Other Texts

Introductory

'. . . I tell them to go and study Sanskrit and Pali before they talk about yoga, Buddhism and reincarnation . . .and to leave me alone until they have read these primary languages for two or three years. . . the difficulty of access is no excuse, for if that were allowed, it would imply that achieving yogic powers and nirvana and wisdom are easier than learning Sanskrit and Tibetan. They are not. '

(Agehananda Bharati, *The Ochre Robe*, 271)

'There's but one God, there's but one Veda,
there's but one initiation by one spiritual guide,
there's but one kind of bliss which he grants,
there's but one human birth in this world.
They who hold the country asserting that
there are four Vedas, and six sects,
and many gods they will surely burn in fiery hell!'

These verses are by a medieval Siddha poet, Konkanar. More about him will be said below in this chapter. Although the above-quoted statement of A Bharati (L. Fischer) sounds rather dictatorial and dogmatic, since it would, if true, invalidate the experience of thouands of Buddhists and others who do not read these 'primary' languages (and hence we can hardly quite agree with it), when it comes to the Siddha texts, a knowledge of Tamil and Sanskrit seems indeed indispensible. Why is it so?

Dealing with Siddha poetic and prosaic texts involves several almost insurmountable difficulties. First of all, there exists no accepted or critically arranged corpus of Siddha writings, not even of Siddha poems. A handy volume in several editions and several different versions (!) exists which is called (usually) Cittar nana-k kovai, literally The Garland of Siddha Wisdom.[1]

Second, what is usually vaguely and generally referred to as Siddha poetry and found in the anthologies contains poems (and texts) of vastly different nature - in attitudes, content, form, diction, prosody. There is great, indeed marvellous poetry of the passionately pessimistic Pattinattar, next to almost childish versification of Pattirakiri, next to deeply religious and vehemently revolutionary Civavakkiyar, next to

---

1 But also *Patinen cittar nana-k kovai*, The Garland of Wisdom of 18 Siddhas, or *Cittar periya nana-k kovai ena valankum Cittar patalkal*, Siddha Poems known as Large Garland of Siddhas' Wisdom. The edition of my esteemed Tamil guru Me. Vi. Venukopala Pillai (1896 - 1985) of 1956 consists of 39 pieces; the edition prepared by Aru. Ramanatan (1959, 1963, 1968) includes 36 pieces. There are other editions (e.g. Ratna Nayakar Publications, 1937). I follow in my selection the 1956 ed. It goes without saying that all these anthologies contain only a small fragment of what could be designated as Siddha writings: they consist mostly of Siddha poetry and some of them include a few prose-texts on medicine/alchemy/hygiene etc., but the enormous bulk of Siddha medical and alchemical texts remains either unedited and unpublished in print, available only on palm-leaves, or (in absolute minority) printed separately. Thus, e.g., a list of texts ascribed to Akattiyar and culled from the Madras University Manuscripts Library, Tanjavur's Saraswathi Mahal Library, and a work by K. Pazhanisami, contains, together with treatises published under his name in print, almost 300 works (!); they deal with yoga, medicine, spells, philosophy etc. About 30 of these have been printed, e.g. on surgery (Palani Devasthanam, 1975), on ophthalmology (ibid. , 1976), on medicial oils (Ratna Naicker, Madras, s.d.), on Akattiyar's 'secret' language (Maignana Vilakku Press, 1962) etc.

profound Konkanar, hardly intelligible Pampatti, and immensely influential, mystical and yet pragmatic, very forceful Tirumular.

Third, the dating of most of the Siddha authors is still to a great extent a matter of anyone's guess, and of disputes. 'Siddhas in the Tamil land trace their origin to Agastya and various works on mysticism, worship, medicine and alchemy are in circulation as having come from his pen. Their language is too modern to be older than the fifteenth century AD.'[2] But who was this Agastya? Since he speaks in several of his medical and alchemical works of syphilis as *parankiviyati* 'the Frankish disease', and of mercury as *paranki pasanam* 'the Frankish mineral', he must be indeed rather 'modern'. But Siddha oral tradition credits him with being the father of the Tamil language, inventor of grammar, enormously skillful surgeon, master of twelve disciples to whom he taught the different arts and sciences, and even early Western scholars like Taylor call him 'the prince of Indian doctors', 'one of India's greatest Philosophers' who 'may perhaps claim to rank on a level with Socrates, or Plato'[3]. He was supposed to have lived in prehistoric times. On the other hand, although most of the Siddha poets do indeed belong to Tamil middle ages (between 14th - 17th centuries), the anthologies of their poetry include important works that can be dated as early as 7th century (Tirumular, referred to by Umapati Civacarya of early 14th century clearly as Siddha), and as late as Ramalinga Svami (1823 - 1874)!

Finally, there is the problem of language and diction of Siddha texts. The technical term for the intentionally enigmatic language of the texts is *samdhyabhasa*, literally 'twilight language'. Due to the fact that Siddha doctrines have been considered an esoteric teaching which may be revealed only by oral instruction, and possibly after initiation, in initiatory manner, the language of these texts is often on purpose ambiguous, dark, metaphorical, semantically polyvalent. The texts can be read with a number of 'keys': liturgical, yogic, Tantrik, but also medical or alchemical or sexological. And yet, on the surface, many of these texts, particularly the poems, read like simple folksongs. Also, their message is usually not stated explicitely or discursively but rather vaguely and indeed enigmatically, in allusions and images. We are

---

2 T. P. Meenakshisundaram, *Notes to Simon Casie Chitty, The Tamil Plutarch*, ed. Colombo, 1946.

3 Taylor's *Oriental Historical Manuscripts*, Vol. I, pp. 172 and 175.

dealing with texts which operate on more than one level of meaning. Thus, e. g. , a stanza from a Siddha treatise which, on the surface level, mentions sun and moon, is interpreted by the 'adept' entirely differently, because moon stands for male semen and sun for 'the blood of women', i. e. menstrual discharge. At the same time, moon/sperm is the essence of Siva, while sun/blood stands for Sakti. The stanza operates in this way on three levels:

surface; whiteness of the moon - vermilion of the sun

Siddha medical level: unity of semen and blood

mystical level: unity of Siva and Sakti

While the philosophic and mystical level deals with the 'conjunction of opposites', with the abolishment of all dualities, with the return to Primeval Unity, the stanza is at the same time an instruction how to act: to take sexual union as ritual, well-known in Tantrik Yoga.

To quote another example: Tirumantiram 806 (826, in chapter on *pariyanka yokam* or 'yoga of the cot') says

' . . . with sexual desire,
Friday [or, planet Venus] will dissolve in Thursday [or, planet Jupiter],
when the female with soft dice-like breasts
and the gambler, being mashy in seed. . . ' etc.

These odd lines, translated into common parlance, say in fact, with sexual desire, the man's semen will dissolve in the female's discharge, when the woman with soft cone-like breasts and the man swoon after ejaculation. . . '

[An additional pun is intended: the female's breasts are similar to conical pieces in dice-game; that's why the male partner is called 'gambler'; and yet in addition, the female is full of 'tricks' and 'devices' in sex-play - another meaning of the word indicating 'dice'. Tirumantiram is replete with stanzas which, as its editor observes, are composed in 'the Siddhas' intentional jargon', adding that seed is also termed 'pepper-water' (known from Anglo-Indian parlance as the soup 'mulligatawny') or 'mercury', and female discharge 'sulphur'.]

We have not yet reached the end. There is yet another level of interpretation of Siddha texts based on sound-symbolism, on metalinguistic understanding of sound. It is necessary in this connection to bring to mind the basic ontological tenets of Tamil Saiva Siddhanta (one of the philosophical roots of Siddha doctrines), namely that sound (*natam*) is more basic (in fact, 'primeval') than either mind or matter. Both mind and matter evolved from sound (*oli*). Hence the tremendous effectiveness of the spoken word, particularly if organized in seemingly meaningless formulae, the spells, the mantras. And yet this is nothing specifically Siddha, but in Siddhism it has been systematically developed. Thus the vowel {a} is viewed as the symbol of life-giving principle, and this symbolism goes as far back as the most popular of all Tamil classical texts, the Tirukkural (cca. 450 A.D.) which begins 'Just as {a} is first among sounds, so the Primeval Lord is first in cosmos.'

In Siddha texts, this has been developed in various ways. Civavakkiyar's stanza 9. 1-2 says, 'He is not Hari, He is not Lord Siva. He is the Ultimate Cause, in the Beyond of Beyond transcending Blackness, Redness and Whiteness.' Tamil: ariyum alla ayanum alla appurattil appuram/karumai cemmai venmaiyai-kkatantu ninra karanam.

Note how the first line is replete with the alliteration of words beginning with the 'primeval sound' {a}: in the Tamil ear, this special 'music' of the first line evokes at once the deepest symbolism going beyond the surface meaning of the Ultimate Cause being neither Hari (= Visnu) nor Ayan (= Siva), and transcending the three colours, black (the colour of the Goddess as Kali; or of Yama, the God of death; or, if taken as black-blue, dark blue, of Visnu), red (the colour of blood and vermillion, i. e. woman, of Goddess as Sakti) and white (the colour of semen and sacred ash, i.e. of male, of Siva); in other words, the Ultimate is completely and absolutely transcendent, and yet immanent.[4]

In the most general sense, one may designate as Siddha poetry any outpouring in Tamil which 'revolted from everything orthodox and ritualistic'. This broadest possible definition would leave us with an enormous volume of poetry which employs with power the spoken language and, although based on a certain trend in Saivism, ridicules

---

4 As indicated, these three colours are pregnant with different connotations: they stand ultimately for the phenomenal world of shapes and colours. White is indeed associated with male creativeness (the colour of semen; *venmai* 'whiteness' being a synonym of *cukkilam* which means both 'whiteness' and 'sperm'), but also with Siva's sacred ash; red, the colour of menstrual blood, with the female principle; black, with the darkness of the womb, of chthonic regions, but also with the venom Siva drank to save the world, and so on and so forth.

orthodox beliefs and customs, and has had, and still has, tremendous impact on the masses.[5]

Our selection is, however, based on more specific criteria. But faced with all that has been said above, we have adopted a pragmatic approach. Taking as our basic text the edition of Siddha texts by one of our esteemed teachers, Mahavidvan M. V. Venugopala Pillai,[6] we shall give brief selections from the eleven most popular or most important texts included in this anthology (which contains all in all 39 texts) in the order adopted there, adding a relatively modern poet (Ramalinga Svami) who has not been included but who may also be regarded legitimately as a Siddha poet at least in some of his works. Thus the following selection will contain specimens of the poetry of Civavakkiyar, Pattinattar, Pattirakiriyar, Pampatti Cittar, Itaikkattu Cittar, Akappey Cittar, Kutampai Cittar, Katuveli Cittar, Alukuni Cittar, Konkanar, Tirumular and Ramalinga, in this order. In addition, only for illustrative purposes, two very brief portions of late-Siddha prose-writings have been included, as well as specimens of medieval Siddha medical treatises.

---

5 M. Arunachalam, *An Introduction to the History of Tamil Literature*, 1974, p. 209.

6 Cittar nana-k kovai (*The Garland of Siddha Wisdom*), Madras, 1956.

Civavakkiyar

According to legend, at his very birth the poet uttered the name of Siva (Tam. Civan) and was therefore called Civavakkiyar, 'one who says "Siva".' However, it is more probable that the poet's name is a back-formation from the name of his text, Civavakkiyam 'Aphorisms on Siva'. It is perhaps significant that almost all editions of Siddha poetry begin with this work. An independent edition of his poems contains 510 stanzas.[7] The dating of the work remains a problem. Since Pattinattar the Earlier (Pattinattatikal) mentions a Civavakkiyatevar (Tiruvitaimarutur mummanikkovai 28. 32-3 in the Saiva canon), it would seem that the poet belonged to an age preceding the 10th century. However, he must have been well-versed in Vedanta and Saiva Siddhanta philosophy; he uses some late (Urdu!) loan-words; he is mentioned by two medieval poets - Tattuvarayar (15th cent.) and Civananavallal (end of 15th c.), and Marainanacampantar quotes him in his commentary. All this assigns our Siddha poet to some period preceding the 15th - 16th centuries, not later, also because he ignores the often antagonistic divisions between Saiva and Vaisnava creeds. The solution is (as so often in Tamil literary historiography) to posit two poets of the same name; an earlier Civavakkiyar mentioned before 10th century,[8] and the Siddha at the end of the 14th - beginning of the 15th c. According to legend, Civavakkiyar was born a Brahmin, took a wife from low community (of the Kuravar), received initiation from a Siddha guru (Konkanar), and performed miracles. He is also supposed to have made pilgrimage to Benares; this motif may be based on a personal allusion occurring in one of his poems.

Civavakkiyar is in many ways the most typical of true Siddha poets, and certainly one of the most forceful. As Arunachalam says, 'Some of his verses have the force of a sabre thrust'[9].

Being one of the great rebels against Hindu and Brahminic establishment and an implacable opponent of the caste system, his poems were not included in the Saiva canonical literature (Tirumurai). The two

---

[7] Ma. Vativelu Mutaliyar (ed. and comment.), Civavakkiyar patal, Madras, 1970. Some other eds. contain as many as 527 st.

[8] The Siddha Civavakkiyar could not have lived before the 10th cent. There are many very strong reasons against such early date (cf. Mu. Arunacalam, Tamil ilakkiya varalaru, 14th cent. , p. 348).

[9] *An Introduction to the History of Tamil Literature*, Tiruchitrambalam, 1974, p. 262.

most typical qualities of his poetry are the contemptuous tone toward sex, and the use of common, even 'vulgar' or obscene speech-forms. Another characteristic feature of his poetry is the awareness of the sounds of Tamil - of linguistic signs - as representing certain basic properties of Reality[10].

Like the various shapes fashioned of one single bullion of gold
Lord Vishnu and Lord Siva as One have entered my heart.
You, so-called learned men, speak of differences and distinctions.
The One Name that pervades everything is just This One Name.
(17/21/28)

Listen
you who take always sacred baths
you who kindle sacrificial fires
you who pour in tons of ghee
hear words of wisdom
hear
The fires
and holy waters
are within
Behold
remember
and attest
An endless
undiminished light
will appear
and union in oneness
be (29)

The Lord came
And entered
And made His shrine
Within my heart.
Like the sweet juice that develops
Within a tender coconut

---

10 In my 1973 book (repr. 1993), 19 poems of Civavakkiyar were published on pp. 80-88.

Seemingly without cause.
After
The Lord came
And entered
And made His shrine
Within my heart
I have not said a thing.
I am silent before men of this world. (30/31)

The Veda you recite is spit. The mantras in it are - spit.
All pleasures are but spit. All seven worlds are - spit.
Honeyed sperm is spit. Intellect is spit. Enlightenment is - spit.
There is nothing, indeed, nothing that is not spit! (42)

Fools!
Immersing yourself in water
You shout:
Pollution! Pollution!
This 'clean' body your temporary abode isn't it
pollution?
Your honeyed drink:
pollution.
Blossoms
polluted by the bees.
As soon as you touch
the pure milk of a cow
with your hand pollution! (471/478)

It is not 'good', it is not 'bad'.
The One Thing is right in the middle.
If you say, It is good - it is good.
If you say, It isn't good, it's evil - it is evil.
Seeking that One Good, just say The Name. (491/498)

You who are foolish
will say:
'These Siddhas are small men.'
You who are foolish
will even think:
These Siddhas are mad.
Yes !
Although they are here,
they live in the realm and sphere
of The Madman.
That's why for them
this world
and His world
are one. (499/506)

Gods made out of wood
Gods made out of stone
Gods made out of palmyra stems
Gods made out of bone
Gods made out of rags
Gods made out of dung
Gods made out of saffron bags
There are no other gods
but
VOID (503/510)

You begging bullocks!
In ochre robes,
with matted hair,
with water-vessels,
rosary-beads and walking sticks,
you have forsaken your women
and roam about the country wide and large
begging for a grain of boiled rice !
Idiots! (511/518)

Pattinattar

In many ways, he was the greatest poet among the Siddhas. In some ways, he is however the least typical among them: it is Pattinattar (14th - 15th century) who is the most pessimistic, the most frustrated, the most cynical and at the same time the most helpless among the Siddhas. There are two legends current in Tamil literary lore about his life. His real name was Tiruvenkata Cettiyar of the rich merchant community, living in the great harbour of Chola kingdom, Kaveri-p-pattinam (hence his nom-de-plume, Pattinattar, 'He who belongs to the City')[11]. One day he received the news of the loss of his ships, but suddenly they were sighted off the shore laden with gold. He ran to the beach to welcome them. During his absence, a Saiva ascetic came to his house begging alms. Pattinattar's wife requested him to wait till her husband's return. Put out with the delay, he gave her an earless needle tied up in a rag with the following note:

Ill-gotten wealth, the miser's hidden treasure,
and even an earless needle
won't serve one on his last
journey.

When the merchant-prince returned, he read these lines, and his life changed then and there. He distributed his riches as alms, renounced his home, and lived as a poor mendicant, causing great scandal in his family and community. Finally, his sister could not bear it any longer. She tried to poison him with some sugared rice-cake, but in vain. He survived and went on composing his great poetry. According to another story, while he was a rich and pious householder he was feeding sumptuously all Saiva devotees. One day a boy was brought to him for sale as a slave, and the merchant-prince treated him as a son and taught him the arts and ways of the trader. The boy did well, and every time he went out for business, he returned home with immense profit. Once, however, he spent everything in building a temple and in alms-giving. When he turned home he filled his boat with cow-dung cakes and took them to the treasury maintaining that each had golden dust mixed with it - and proved it by dissolving one in water. In spite of this feat he was imprisoned, but due to a few miracles performed in the prison the adoptive father came to the

[11] This lively port was known to Ptolemaios and other Greek and Roman historiographers as Khaberis Emporion. In imperial times, Romans and Greeks kept intensive overseas trade-relations with the port.

conclusion that the prisoner was Siva incarnate. The boy was released, and the merchant sat at his feet and by means of an earless needle reached enlightenment. At once he turned ascetic, went from shrine to shrine composing his poems, and ultimately settled in Tiruvorriyur near Madras in company with simple cowherds. He begged them to bury him every day up to his shoulders and release him only at nightfall. This rigorous asceticism proved fatal. One day the cowherds ran away home to avoid a heavy shower, forgetting all about him; next morning he was found dead.

One of the features of his poetry is his pathological hatred of women, in contrast with most (if not all) other Siddhas, some of them, as said above, sharing in their attitude to sex rather the views and even methods of Tantrism. For Pattinattar, the female body is a bag of filth. The belly, compared by poets to a banyan leaf, is shaking bag of dirty dregs; the breasts, compared to lotus-buds are dried-up pouches parched by inner heat and scratched by lewd fingernails of lusty men. Their seat of pleasure is a chasm 'wherefrom sprouts and spurts/copious pus/and bloody discharge/and slimy mucus' (Potu 14); they smell of their sensuality (31). Man's body (including the poet's own) is no better: 'full of lust and lechery/Its towering weapon/swelling into skies ' (55). What striking contrast to the care devoted to the body by Siddha physicians who strived after its health, longevity and physical 'immortality'! Many stanzas ascribed to Pattinattar raise doubts about the tradition which classifies him with the Siddhas. There are indeed certain features - even phrases and metaphors - which he shares with the other poets of the school; thus e.g. the formulaic image of life compared in its impermanence to the bubble on the surface of water: it is found in Pattirakiri, Pattinattar, Katuveli Cittar, etc. etc. His greatest poem, 'The Harmony of the Component Parts of Human Body'[12] in 24 stanzas is a hymn on human life from conception and birth to death, full of sadness, resignation and humility, as great as Shakespeare's famous verses in As You Like It II. 7, as mercilessly true as the pronouncements of the Buddha on impermanence and dukkha.[13] According to M.

---

[12] The entire poem was published in my 1973 (1993) book pp. 102- 107. On death, cf. ibid. p. 68.

[13] In my 1973 (1993) book, 16 poems of Pattinattar were published on pp. 93 - 107.

Arunachalam,[14] 'Till recently, there was no mendicant beggar or wandering minstrel who did not sing a dozen of his verses to the accompaniment of an one-stringed self-made harp.'

In my desire of the earth the earth has devoured me; and so
the desire for gold and the desire for women won't leave me, no!
(Arutpulampal 6)

Lust and aversion won't go, won't leave me; they vow:
'It's we that reign!' And they daily grow. (Ibid. 13)

I haven't yet conquered my ego, and fright.
I haven't yet shaken off my heart-burning pride! (Ibid. 15)

Sugar-cane breasts say,
'We'll ruin your soul.'
Blossom-like eyes say,
'We'll devour you whole.' (Ibid. 17)

And her cunt - cobra's hood - says,
'I'll ruin you, my knave.'
And yet for its hellish pit
I still do crave. (Ibid. 18)

O Lord Ekampa of Kacci!
A demon of delusion came
in the shape of a woman
and got me -
ensnared me with her eyes,
bewitched me with her breasts,
sucked me in
into the wound of her hollow
womb
under the hill of her loins
to rob me of the treasure
of my wisdom -

---

14 *An Introduction to the History of Tamil Literature*, Tiruchitrambalam, 1974, p. 262.

and I forgot
you
(Tiruvekampamalai 23)

Now listen, my heart!
Even the mother's love
is an enemy!
The women one took -
greater enemy!
Even one's children
are enemies.
One's kith and kin - enemies.
In fact - this whole world
is an enemy.
Searching one's soul
one rejects possessions and thereafter FREEDOM!
At the golden feet
of the Lord of Marutur.
(Tiruvitaimarutur 2)

Breasts that deceive.
Women who copulate.
Wealth which burdens.
In our final battle
what is their use?
Perhaps
because of merit done,
and to truly know,
the Undeceiving Lord
today
threw
an eyeless needle
in my hand. (Potu I. 9)

There's cool dew for your patched rags to wash whenever you wish,
There's some rice in every house for you to eat to beg for every day,
If you're aroused there are fine whores to be had in every street,
Why then should you grow weary and always worry, my heart ?
(Potu I. 15)

There's a river, a grove, there's even a shady hall in the market street,
There's the sacred ash, and a proper loin-cloth made of rags,
There's food to eat in each house as you roam about changing streets,
And then there's sleep. O my confused heart! Be calm and quiet.
Happiness. (Potu I. 16)

I enjoyed having herds of cattle and children But they are perdition and ruin.
I lost them - and now,
listen, my heart - now
there's the begging bowl
and the rags
and the sacred five-letter mantra
to sing
and the slaves of the Lord Who Drank the Poison, they, indeed, are our fellows and friends. (Potu I. 18)

The Absolute
unconfined to the four old Vedas
has come and reached me
here.
I touched the state
of Undiminished Truth.
I am
beyond
pleasure or pain.
I don't care
about good or evil.
I have no time
for useless fellows.
I don't listen
to their empty talk.
I have left
the world. (Potu I. 24)

[Imagining his funeral. Traditionally, one's son, preferably, circumambulates the body, and breaking the pot with fire sets fire to the pyre. - Golden *tali* = marriage badge worn round the neck by married women .]

The mother who bore me despised me saying, 'A corpse! '
The woman who wore my golden tali, said, 'Go!'- and then cried.
My grown-up children went round my body and broke the pot.
O Lord, apart from your embrace there is no love! (Potu I. 28)

[The Three Cities of the demons were burnt by god Siva. Southern Lanka was burnt by Hanuman, friend and ally of Rama.]

Fire
set upon the Three Cities
once
Then
fire
set upon Southern Lanka
Fire
set upon my mother's pyre
It burns in my heart
Fire
set by me for her. Let it catch
and burn well (Potu II. 7)

Pattirakiriyar

His name is probably to be connected with Sanskrit Bhadragiri (or with Bhartrhari?). Legend says that he was a king who renounced his kingdom and taking Pattinattar as his guru, embraced Siddha teachings. He was meek and mild, and performed menial services for his fierce preceptor. His Meynnana pulampal ('Lamentations for True Knowledge') is a collection of 231 - 237 couplets, all of them ending in the words *e-k-kalam* 'when?'. They express pathetic and yet passionate longing for deliverance, peace, sleep of death - stanzas of 'high-pitched wailing'[15]; but they always show his love for fellow-beings, although he, too, feels fear of and aversion towards women.[16]

When will come
the time
when I shall think of women as mothers,
be quiet like a corpse,
and rove about like a ghost? (8)

When will come
the time
when I'll cease to think with longing and joy
of money-bags, pleasures, palaces,
palanquins, ploys? (20)

When will come
the time
when I'll forsake this transient life,
this bubble of water,
in floods of compassion
released by your love? (62)

When will come
the time
when, crossing the ocean of lust
and reaching safe shores,
my heart will kindle and feed

---

[15] C. and H. Jesudasan, *A History of Tamil Literature*, 1961, p. 227.
[16] *The Poets of the Powers* (1973, 1993) contains 7 stanzas (pp. 89 - 90).

sacrificial fires? (145)

Is it now
the time
to listen in worship and love,
hearing the holy anklet ringing
in Siddhi's sacred dance?(194)

Pampatti Cittar

He is the most popular of all Tamil Siddha poets, one of the most outspoken, even crude, among them, but he has not much common with the Siddhas as physicians/alchemists. There is no medical treatise ascribed to him apart from one toxicological work, *Cittararutam* (which is probably anyhow not his). 'The Siddha With the Dancing Snake' (that's what his name means) is the author of some 300 stanzas speaking of the rejection of wealth and women, and teaching how to attain Siddhahood and liberation. The Kundalini Sakti lies coiled like a snake, and the Siddha invokes her and tells her to 'rise and dance'. I give below the translation of his best known stanzas (20, 22), sung till this day by all Tamilians[17].

[The snake, truly polyvalent in Hindu symbolism, is in this poem symbol of the Goddess, and of Sakti, the Potence and Energy of the Cosmos; it is also thought of as adorning the matted hair of Siva; Siva also has snake(s) for earrings, and Vishnu, the god of Maintenance and Preservation, has the broad hood of a cobra as shading parasol, and goddess Parvati, the daughter of the Himalaya and Siva's consort, has snakes as bracelets. Snake is the lord of the chthonic regions, of the Earth, and his poison has the power to destroy but also to heal.]

Rise and dance and rise and dance
oh Playful Snake
Coiled upon the crown of Siva
Naga Snake
Keeping ready fangs of poison
Cobra Snake
Crawling into hellish regions
Hooded Snake (20)

You've become Lord Siva's earrings
Faultless Lord
You've become the shade for Vishnu
Vishnu's Parasol
You've become Parvati's bracelets

[17] *The Poets of the Powers* (1973, 1993) contains 15 pieces of this Siddha (pp. 114 - 19). Cf. also an excellent study of D. Buck, 'The Snake in the Song of a Sittar', *Structural Approaches to South Indian Studies*, 1974, 162- 83.

Tangled Hair
Do not hide but dance in joy
Oh snake Oh snake (22)

[In the above poem, the translation tried to closely imitate the rhythm of the original, as it is heard being sung in Tamil India. The following poem is of completely different nature, and shows the poet's attitude to women.]

She's a peacock, a nightingale, a ruby,
a doe, honey, heavenly nectar, a jewel,
she walks like a graceful gazelle. Snake,
don't fall under her spell,
don't praise her,
but rather scold and master her,
and dance,
O snake! (56)

7. God Murugan with his two consorts (Valli and Devasena) a favourite deity of most Siddhas (c.: e.g. the poetry of Ramalinga Svami). Probably of Dravidian (pre-Aryan) origin. Traditional South Indian print.

Itaikkattuccittar

'The Siddha of the Pasture-Forest' (15th century?) belonged, so the tradition maintains, to the Itaiyar or cowherd caste, and indeed the tone and imagery of his stanzas suggest pastoral milieu. Some of the 130 stanzas of his song are conceived as dialogues between two shepherds, Narayana Konar and Tantavaraya Konar. They are often filled with theistic devotion.[18]

O gentle cow!
Even if I had everything -
if I had not the Lord's Grace,
you can think of me as one
who has
nothing. (37)

O gentle cow!
Apart from God's help
there's nothing to be sought.
The Holy Feet of the Father
are the very breath of Life. (38)

O honey-bee, fly.
Vanished Ignorance.
O honey-bee, fly!
We've glimpsed total Bliss!
O honey-bee, fly!
We've realized Truth.
O honey-bee, fly to your nest,
We've climbed the very Mountain Crest! (52)

Dance, O peacock, dance!
See? Our Ancient Serpent! Dance!
O peacock, strutting on the ancient path to the Nest,
proceed without fail in silence,
without fail. (87)

---

[18] *The Poets of the Powers* (1973, 1993) contains 12 pieces of this Siddha (pp. 108 - 9).

Sound your flute, shepherd,
sound your flute
to scare away
tigers who
draw near
the flocks of your sheep! (101)

Akappey Cittar

'The Siddha [who invokes] the Demon of the Heart' is one of the later Siddha poets (15th century or later).[19] His 90 stanzas, deeply mystical, are composed in very simple language and very simple form. They offer an exposé of Siddha doctrines and instructions, from a vision of the evolution of the universe and man to a total mystical 'nihilism' in the acceptance of Pure Void (*cuniyam*). Often, however, the stanzas are coached in *sandhabhasha*, intentionally dark language with double entendres as in 47 where *intu* 'moon' means simultaneously male semen and *iravi* 'sun' stands for menstrual blood.

The spurt of sperm
and her fluid juices
became solid body.
It's but the seat
of the five main elements.(4)

All these various forms and shapes
are NOT my Lord!
THAT Form is very different.
Although you seek and search
you will not see it. (19)

The Moon is nectar.
The Sun is - poison?
The 'moon' shimmers white.
The 'sun' is RED. (47)

'That' is not male. Nor female either.
You have gazed at fire.
It is the Shelter's Shaft.
You've seen the Lord of Life. (48)

---

[19] The 1973 (1993) book contains 5 stanzas ascribed to this poet (p. 110).

Kutampaiccittar

'The Siddha with the Earthen Ring'[20] is author of some 32 stanzas addressed to the earthen ring which is for him the (female) symbol of the soul. He speaks of ultimate reality as *vettaveli* 'sheer/clear light' (can also be interpreted as 'absolute void') or *uyarveli* 'the highest light' (or 'highest emptiness').[21] Most of his stanzas, cast in simple form and language, are in fact metaphors and symbols. He occasionally uses typical Siddha symbolism of various spices, herbs, plants and remedies.[22] All of the stanzas are rhetorical questions.

To those who've gone beyond death,
to those who go their own way,
what is the use of worship and rites,
(O earthen ring),
what is the use of worship and rites? (13)

To those who burst with bliss,
to those who're eternally wise,
what is the use of mere knowledge,
(O earthen ring),
what is the use of mere knowledge? (15)

If you rove about town all day,
rambling and roaming and won't stay,
what is the use of having a veil,
(O earthen ring),
what is the use of having a veil? (29)

---

20 *Kutampai* is an earthen ring worn by Tamil women to widen the perforation in their ear-lobes.

21 In spoken Tamil, *vettaveliccam* means 'broad daylight' but also something quite evident. However, if we take *veli* as connected etymologically rather with DEDR 5498 'outside, open space, space, openess' (than with DEDR 5496), the expression may be interpreted as 'sheer Emptiness, total Void'.

22 Thus he will mention onion, pepper, dry ginger, mango-juice, coconut milk. In the 1973 (1993) book, 5 stanzas of this poet are included on pp. 111-12.

Katuveliccittar

'The Siddha of Absolute Void' (or, 'Ethereal Sky') is author of 34 stanzas, all with the following refrain: 'O heart, remain pure and sinless/tomorrow comes the angry God of Death to fetch you.' His stanzas are pessimistic and moralizing. In st. 3 he uses the well-known image of 'this body, a bubble on the surface of water'.

Ascend the Path of True Wisdom.
Search for pure Vedanta in the Absolute Void,
Forsake the way of ignorance and doubt.
Reveal to your friend the Way of Bliss. (10)

Shall this past karma disappear in Kasi?
Shall salvation come of itself while plunging into Ganga?
Shall former actions perish by mere talk and prattle?
Shall former discords go, even in graceful birth? (15)

Don't dress in the garb of tricks.
Don't plunge your body in so many Gangas.
Don't think of grabbing, robbing, plunder.
Don't waste the time in slander, talk with friends. (33)

Alakaniccittar (alias Alukuniccittar)

One of those Siddha poets of whom we know nothing at all. There is a vague tradition current that he was opium-eater. The name is sometimes explained as (1) the Siddha of 'beauty' (*alaku*) and rhetoric skill (*ani* 'ornament, rhetoric') since his poetry is supposed to be beautiful and accomplished; or as (2) the Weeping Siddha (*alukuni* means 'weeping, crying person' even in ordinary parlance). Author of just 32 stanzas, rather complex in form in the *kali* metre. They are all rhetoric questions addressed to 'my Kannamma', a kind of divine sweetheart of Krishnaite background. Two specimens must suffice.

Have I become a rotten tree
having forgotten thee?
Those who have forgotten themselves -
for those there's not even their mother, their father.
If there's at least a mother for those
who haven't forgotten themselves,
won't I be living in peace and bliss
since I haven't forgotten thee,
O my Kannamma? (28)

I said, 'If I eat the fruit of a plantain,
my mouth will ache.'
Having eaten the fruit of a wild thorny shrub
I died.
Having forsaken the fruit of the wild thorny shrub
I have recovered.
Shall I die,
if now I eat the fruit of the plantain,
o my Kannamma?
Won't I live? (9)

Konkana Nayanar

One of the most colourful and most important of the early Siddha poets. Supposed to have lived in the 7th century AD. He goes under many names (Konkana Cittar, Konkana Natar, Tevar, Nayakar) as author of medical, alchemical and yogic treatises, who originated from the Konku country (around today's Coimbatore). Some traditions designate him as disciple of the famous Pokar (Bhoga) of Pazhani. He seems to have been a truly historical person. According to one legendary account, when his master Pokar became enchanted with a certain woman and could not succeed to get hold of her, Konkanar transformed a statue into the live woman and brought her to his master to enjoy her. Another story says that one day when Konkanar went begging he rested during the midday heat under a tree. As he was resting, a heron let its droppings fall on the sage's head, and Konkanar gazed at it angrily, whereupon the poor bird was burnt to ashes by the sage's fierce look. Only thus found out Konkanar his boundless power. He then entered the house of the famous poet Tiruvalluvar whose wife Vasuki let him wait for some time before she offered him alms. When, angry again, he threw her one of his fierce glances she just laughed and said: 'Do you think that I am a miserable heron?' He was much ashamed and his haughtiness diminished considerably. His best-known work is *Konkanar nanam*, a treatise against polytheism. He is also author of 111 stanzas called *Valaikkummi*.

The first word designates a girl who has not yet attained the age of puberty and, at the same time, Sakti, the Goddess (cf. Sanskrit *bala-*). The second words designates a female dance with clapping of hands to time and singing, and a poem composed in such rhythm. Some of his forceful verses are no mean poetry.

Dance, all of you, women,
the Tamil of that beloved Konganar,
sing, all of you, Siddhas,
worship that harlot Valai,
with song and dance! (1)

This stanza is interesting and revealing: It seems that the puritanism of some Indian editors has hit this stanza, too. In its last line, the text[23] says clearly *valai-p-parattai-pporri* 'praise in worship Valai the harlot'; some editors, e.g. Va. Caravanamuttu Pillai, changed *parattai* 'harlot' into *patattai* 'feet' ('praise in worship the feet of Valai'). Two crucial stanzas about Siddha worship follow:

Let us attend on the one-tusked child Vinayaka,
remover of illusion, support of wisdom,
singing with loud voices the kummi of the Best Woman,
that young maid Valai who is Sakti Parvati! (2)

Let us attend on the golden feet of Pattini
Sarasvati dancing in wild rhythm,
singing with loud voices the kummi of that Sakti,
the young maid Valai who's worshipped by all Siddhas! (3)

The one-tusked child Vinayaka is Ganapati or Ganesa with the elephant-head, the youthful god who is remover of all obstacles (should any work be undertaken without worship of Ganesa, obstacles will inevitably occur); he has only one tusk which is the support of all existence. Kummi is a joyful, playful song-dance of women. Valai is the young goddess who is Sakti (primeval Energy, Dynamism) who is also Parvati (daughter of the Himalaya) the consort of Siva, and Pattini, the perfect female and perfect wife as well as Sarasvati, goddess of arts, learning, speech and wisdom. The designation of Valai as harlot is meaningful: it is the technique termed in cultural anthropology 'praise through blame' but, more importantly, as parattai, harlot who belongs to every man and no man, she is the all-embracing female beyond any limitations and boundaries of 'good' and 'evil', 'proper' and 'improper'. Very important is the line which describes Valai as worshipped and praised by all Siddhas.

Without the earth there is no sky,
without at least a bit of fragrance there is no flower.

---

23 The edition of Aru. Ramanatan (3rd printing, 1968, p. 255) which maintains to be based on critical collation of manuscripts (performed by Vidvan Na. Tevanattan) has the version with *parattai*.

Without women there are no men.
Think of it, and take care of it, Young Maid ! (72)

You speak of caste distinctions.
Is there any division in the one body of god?
Thick milk which is one stuff
of butter, curd and butter-milk! (95)

Tirumular

Of probably 7th century, saint, seer, poet, mystic, spiritual father of the Tamil Siddha tradition, believed to be incarnation of Siva's sacred bull Nandin. According to later legends, well-known all over South India, he went on a pilgrimage to many Hindu holy places till he reached a green village by the sacred river Kaviri called Sattanur. There he befriended a simple cowherd called Mulan. One day the cowherd died, and his cows gathered around his body shedding tears. The aged yogin left his old body in the forest, and for the sake of the animals entered the dead body of Mulan and tended the cows with great affection. However, Mulan had a young wife, and when her husband was not returning home, she went to search for him, and found 'him' sitting under a tree. She touched respectfully his feet and addressed him as her husband, but the sage said: 'I am not your husband. I have no wife and no home, no attachments.' The wife returned to the village, wailing out her grievances: 'My husband has deserted me!' The villagers gathered round the sage, and a wise man recognized in him a Siddha. Tirumular had to remain in the cowherd's body, but was sitting in silent meditation at Tiruvavatuturai where he composed the 3000 stanzas of Tirumantiram, one stanza every year.

The work consists of quatrains in *kaliviruttam* metre. Modern editions have between 3047 - 3071 stanzas in 232 chapters. Although still a little-studied text, it is a many-layered and many-levelled encyclopaedia of authentic spiritual experience, and probably the one Indian mystical poem that does not only record such experience but also teaches an elaborate technique to reach the goal of that experience. In fact, its author suggests the exact strategy and mechanisms how to reach different states of consciousness.

First chapter, the General Preface, consists of 11 parts: invocation (1) which begins with the famous dictum *onravan tane* 'He is indeed One' and proclaims absolute worship of Civan (Siva), speaking in terms of Saiva Siddhanta[24] (*natan* 'Lord' or *pati* 'Master', *pacu* 'soul', *pacam* 'bondage', these three entities being eternal), 50 stanzas; on Trinity (i.e. Aran, Ari, Ayan - Siva as Hara, Vishnu and Brahma) as well as on Siva and Sakti (2), 10 stanzas; on greatness of the Veda (3), 6 stanzas; on greatness of the Agamas (4), 7 stanzas; on Brahmins (5), 10 stanzas; on

[24] The term Siddhanta (*cittantam*) is used for the first time in Tamil in st. 963 and elsewhere in this text.

kingship (7), 10 stanzas; on heavenly abodes (8), 2 stanzas; on dharma (9), 10 stanzas; on a-dharma (10), 10 stanzas; on modesty of author (11), 2 stanzas. This is followed by Specific Preface on the lineage of the guru (1), 6 stanzas, and on the poet's biography (2), 22 stanzas, in which the poet says; 'After I entered, by the grace of Nandin, the [body of] Mulan, by the grace of Nandin I became Eternal Being; by the grace of Nandin I united with True Knowledge; by the grace of Nandin I was' (st. 156); st. 152 contains the famous line about God (*iraivan*) creating the poet 'well' so that he may '[re]create Him well in Tamil'. Tirumantiram proper begins with the First Tantra of 17 sections (166 stanzas) which is also termed The Agama of First Principles. It deals with *aram* (dharma), the cosmic and moral order. With st. 159, the author begins philosophic discourse on *pati* 'the Lord', *pacu* 'the Cow (= soul)' and *pacam* 'bondage'. He enquires into the state of body and soul, and mentions the three obstacles - lust, anger and confusion. True knowledge is the knowledge of Siva; but a distinction is made between Siva, the personalized God, and *civam*, impersonal godhead, also called 'lustre' (*coti, cutar*), symbolized by Siva's theriomorphic form, the bull Nandin who had planted his feet of grace and entered the poet. The personalized God is often referred to as the divine potter. The devotional element may also be found in this section, in particular in the doctrine of *anpu* 'love' for godhead (often quoted stanza 257). Second Tantra has 25 sections (208 stanzas). It is largely theological, cosmological and 'historical' (mentioning the Akattiyar myth, quoting Lingapuranam, myths of Takkan-Daksa, etc.). Tennatu, South India, is spoken of as the land of Lord Siva who is the Creator, the god of the three actions (creating - preserving - destroying the cosmos, e.g. 391). God Murugan-Skanda, of special significance to Tamil Siddhas, is discussed in stanzas 503 ff.

The Third Tantra (The Heroic Agama, 333 poems) is most important for the development of Siddha movement. It contains the analysis of 'restraints' (*yama*, 535-6) and 'disciplines' (*niyama*, 537-9) - preliminary steps to asceticism; of body postures (*irukkai*, 540 -5), yogic respiration (546-58), emancipation of sensory activities from domination by external objects (*pratyahara*, 559 - 67), concentration (*dharana*, 568 - 77), meditation (*dhyana, ninaital*, 578 - 97) and enstasis (*samadhi, noccippu*, 598 - 611). Thus the categories of physiological - spiritual practices are dealt with in the classical order of Patanjali (Yogasutras II. 29). In addition, the text deals with the results of yoga (612 ff.) and with the eight great occult powers (the *mahasiddhis*, 620 - 91). Further, the text treats some aspects of Tantrik yoga such as *kecari yokam* (*khecari*, 779 - 804) 'simultaneous arresting of the mobility of breath, thought and sperm', *amuritaranai* (825 - 30) 'arresting of urine' etc. [25]

The Fourth Tantra (530 stanzas) deals, roughly speaking, with sacred/magic formulas/spells (mantra) and with cakras. The most important mantra is of course *civayanama* (Sivayanama) which transforms 'copper into gold' (883) etc.; it is played with in many poems (e.g. 903). The mantras and the magic diagrams (cakra, *cakkaram*) are treated in minutest detail, and the text thus provides the student with immensely rich data on medieval Hindu magic.

The Fifth Tantra (154 poems) deals mainly with the moral order, with asceticism, various stages in the development of the spiritual discipline etc.

The Sixth Tantra (128 poems) is devoted to Saivism as the path to immortality.

The Seventh Tantra (407 stanzas) speaks mostly of worship of Siva in the form of the lingam. Although in the shape of male generative organ, and often regarded as phallus, lingam is not anthropomorphic or priapic; its erect shape indicates retention of seed, not emission; it speaks of complete control, and hence is symbolic of the asceticism of Siva who, strictly speaking, may be worshipped only under this symbol.[26] The text mentions different kinds of lingam and different kinds of *puja* (ritualistic worship).

The Eight Tantra (518 quatrains) is very rich and variegated. It deals with gnoseology, philosophy and devotion to God.

The last Tantiram (400 poems) is a brilliant summary of Tantrik mysticism. Its 8th chapter ('The Darshan of the Holy Dance')[27] describes for the first time in Tamil cultural history in great detail Siva-Nataraja's dance in Citamparam (maintaining, however, that the Lord's dance covers everything: 'Everywhere is the Sacred Form, everywhere is Siva's

---

[25] For detailed description of this part of the text cf. my 1973 (1993) publication, 76 - 79.

[26] Cf. the insightful remark of Agehananda Bharati (*op. cit.* 245): 'in the life of sentient beings, only the state of total sexual consummation is desireless, hence again the symbolism of the *linga* '.

[27] The word darshan means literally 'sight, vision'. It is the act of beholding a powerful, or outstanding, or saintly person; or the deity in the temple (or in a dream). It confers merit. Indians speak of 'having darshan', i. e. having a glimpse of a charismatic someone.

Sakti/Citamparam is everywhere, everywhere is the Holy Dance ', 2674. 1- 2).

The strategy adopted by Tirumular is first to impress the practitioner with the impermanence and evanescence of youth, health, wealth and life. Doctrinally, in his religious outlook, he is a rather catholic Saivite. In his philosophy, he is basically Saiva Siddhantin with traces of Advaita. According to him, godhead, soul and material world are eternally existent and uncreated, but a unity of individual soul and godhead is possible. In his practice, Tirumular is a Tantrik yogin: the easiest way how to approach the Unconditioned is in and through the human body which is the seat of the divine: 'After wandering over the lands far and wide, I discovered our Lord in the land of this body.' But a guru's guidance is necessary, as well as initiation into the Unitive Way which is a secret psychosomatic discipline completely independent of external ritualism and worship. In fact, he ridicules the externals of religion and unites the approach of yoga (which he expounds in great detail) with 'the yoga of the cot' (*paryankayoga*), i.e. with the use of sex. In using sex, the practitioner is encouraged to make uninhibited response to bodily demands in order to sublimate these demands into spiritual bliss. It is dangerous, declares Tirumular, to impose any restraint on the senses. At the moment when body is lost, experience comes to an end and, as a consequence, the opportunity of emancipation ends, too. Hence, health of the body is a means to a spiritual end. By God's grace Tirumular has acquired the eight great 'powers', and he is willing to share some of these magic techniques (e.g. there are 30 stanzas in which detailed instruction is given how to enter the body of another person). Many such stanzas have more than one layer of meaning. Apart from being the great forerunner of the Siddha tradition, a Tantrik yogin and a master of spiritual discipline, he is also a worshipper of Siva-Nataraja - the Lord of Dance. However, he homologizes his body and the body of the dancing god. Sometimes one is in doubt whether indeed Tirumantiram is the work of one author or rather of an entire group of Tantrik yoga-philosophers, some of them more interested in medicine, alchemy, magic, others rather in iconography, ritual etc., and yet others in philosophy and theology. There is however a common tone of rugged coarseness; explosive power; finality of statement; and this gives the work unity and authenticity of possibly one single authorship.[28]

The Lord has created me
And created me well
In order that
I may create Him in Tamil
And create Him well
He is One indeed. His sweet Grace makes it Two.
He abides within Three. He woke up in fourfold way.
He conquered the five, evolved in six, transcended
seven, exists in eightfold realization.

This first introductory stanza which begins *Onravan tane* contains an entire theology. Its orthodox, Vedic-Brahminic interpretation: The Godhead, the Unconditioned, is one. With its Grace (*arul*), 'he' is two. He abides in three universal principles - the dim (neutral), the dark and the light (good). He 'woke up' as the four Vedas (there are of course other interpretations, see below). He has conquered the five senses. He evolved within the six paths to liberation: sounds, words, mantras, arts, philosophy and worldly activities. He went beyond the seven heavenly bodies - the Sun, the Moon, Mars, Mercury, Jupiter, Venus, Saturn, i.e. He is transcendent. But He is also immanent: He exists in the eight qualities or attributes (*guna*).

Another interpretation (Saiva Siddhantin): Siva is one. Together with his Sakti (Ammai) he is two. He abides within the three genders (he - she - it). He reveals himself in fourfold way - in morality (ethics), austerities (ascesis), union (devotion, bhakti) and wisdom. He 'conquered' with the help of five scriptures: three collections of canonical Saivite poems (Tevaram), the poetic work of Manikkavacakar, and the Tirumantiram of Tirumular. He 'spread out' (i.e. revealed) to

---

28 Cf. B. Nadarasan, *Tirumantiram* with English Translation, Madras, Kumaraguruparam Press, s. d. , Arunachalam, M. , 'The Mysticism of Tirumular', Ind. Philos. Annual, 11, 1976; Dandapani Desikar, S., *Introduction to Tirumular's Tirumantiram*, Adheenam Publ. 97-A, Tiruvavaduthurai, 1956; Wayne, Surdam, 'The Poetry of Tirumular', *Proceedings, 5th Intern. Conference Seminar of Tamil Studies*, Vol. 2, Madras, 1981, 7a - 41-50.

beings the sixfold transcendental knowledge. He stands beyond the sevenfold birth (is transcendent) and exists like the eight qualities or attributes in all creatures (immanent).

The ignorant say that love and God are two.
They do not know that love itself is God.
Whoever knows that love itself is God
Shall rest in love, one with God.

Those who don't hold fast to the Guru who would heal their blindness
will hold to the guru who won't heal their blindness.
One blind man and another blind man will dance in blindness.
One blind man and another blind man will fall into the pit.

The bones may be used as firewood,
and the flesh cut up and roasted on fire
until it becomes aglow like gold.
Yet except for those who melt with love
and are stirred in the depth of their soul,
the Jewel, resplendent like the sun,
is impossible of attainment.
(Transl. A. J. Appasamy)

She has cooked for him,
he eats to his heart's content,
he copulates with her
and then he says,
'There's pain in my chest. '
He lays down to rest
and lo! he's dead and gone.
(Transl. S. Maharajan, transl. adapted)

Knowledge comes not but for balanced minds.
For balanced minds there is no hell.
Like the great gods will be balanced minds.
I too cling to the path of balanced minds.

A huge drunk elephant hid the tree;
the huge drunk elephant vanished behind the tree;

the base elements of the universe hid the Absolute;
the base elements of the universe vanished in the Absolute.

At the junction of six roads
the sweet sap oozes of the four palmyra palms.
I placed a ladder so that I could climb.
I climbed the palm, and saw the seven oceans.

Once I thought the body was
something vulgar and mean.
But now I know that within this body
and only through it
can I get at Reality.

[On control of the flow of male seed]
Lest the silver should melt
And flow into the gold
The cunning goldsmith
Closes the passage with coal.

[The most famous quatrain of Tirumular as far as medicine and healing is concerned is no. 80:]

Medicine is that which heals the disease of the body.
Medicine is that which heals the disease of mind.
It is that which prevents disease to arise.
Medicine is that which denies death.

This quatrain is of extreme importance for the entire development of Siddha medicine since it contains, in a canonical text, four basic Siddha tenets: One, medicine, medical treatment (*maruntu*) is used, naturally, to 'deny' (*maruppatu*) physical, bodily disease (*utal noy*); second, it is also used to cure diseases of the mind (*ulanoy*); the Siddhas, in their firm belief in the intimate connection, in fact, in the interdependent unity of body-mind, saw as one of the main tasks of medicine psychotherapy. Third, medicine should prevent disease from arising (literally 'deny disease to arise') - in other words, preventative medicine is at least as important as cure. Finally, medical treatment should be directed towards denial of death (*maruppatu cavai*) - hence the preoccupation with longevity and the quest of physical 'immortality'.

8. God Murugan in his shape of Subramanya-Skanda, Lord of War, destroying evil, illness, death (favourite deity of some Siddhas). Traditional South Indian Print.

Ramalinga Svami (Iramalinka Cuvamikal), 1823 - 1874.

The greatest Tamil poet of the 19th century was above all an exponent of Saiva devotionalism, author of thousands of poems and some prose-writings, the poems being reflections of deep mystic experience, and pleas for universal love and harmony. However, particularly towards the end of his life, Ramalinga's powerful and often lovely poetry approached in an ever increasing manner the ideology of the Tamil Siddha movement, in particular in two respects: the search (and achievement?) of 'immortality' in the present life, and in the sphere of social consciousness. In late 1873, disappointed by his followers who stayed away from his ideals of the free flow of spiritual life, untrammelled by divisions of caste, colour or creed, he stayed exclusively at Sittivalakam ('Abode of Siddhi'), and on 30.1.1874 he is reported to have delivered his final discourse before entering a small room locked up from outside. The text of his last discourse says: 'Friends, I opened a shop but there was none to purchase. So I have closed it. I will not be visible to your eyes for a certain period, although I will be universally present in the world. My imperishable body will enter into the bodies of all living beings. I will re-appear again at the proper time after having preached my message in other countries. . . Worship God in the form of light and attain salvation.'[29]

As far as his social attitudes are concerned, in one of his poems he says quite clearly: 'The four *varnas*,[30] the orders of life,[31] all the stories and philosophies proclaimed are but a childish play.' And he describes his personal feeling about the socio-economic set-up of his time in these words; 'I cannot for a moment stand the trials and tribulations of the poor in this whole world. I cannot any longer see or hear anyone in distress.'

For our topic are more important the pronouncements and the many poems which reflect undoubtedly Ramalinga's desire to achieve immortality (*maranam illamai*) and those songs filled with ecstatic joy at

---

[29] Are these ravings of a deluded mind or attempts at a prophetic vision? Cf. S. R. V. Arasu, *Voice of Vallalar, Kazhagam*, Madras, 1974, 55-6.

[30] The fourfold system of basic social hierarchy, valid for all Hindus since Vedic times, of Brahmins, warriors, merchants and labourers. The Siddhas, in agreement with the Buddha, denied its validity.

[31] Tamil *acciramam* < Sans. *asrama-*, four basic orders or stages of life. The combined doctrine of classes and orders is called *varnasrama dharma*. According to the orthodox Hindu view, the a-dharma, i.e. the interference or repudiation of this system, is the forerunner of chaos, is 'unrighteousness'.

the conviction that indeed he has received the boon (*varam*) of deathlessness from his God. It is of no use to try to explain off these pronouncements as symbolic or metaphoric phrases. Consider pronouncements like these: 'Whatever state is indestructible I desire'; 'O Lord, . . . I learned from you that the knowledge (*kalvi*) to study is that of eternal nondying (*enrun cakata*)'; 'This rotten body changed into perfect gold'; perfectly clear are these words: 'I've seen the Father, I've received the boon of deathlessness',[32] and again,

'I've obtained for myself the boon of immortality'.[33]

An entire collection of songs, 28 stanzas, entitled (by the editor of the saint's work, Uranatikal) Deathless Great Life,[34] is devoted exclusively to the subject of immortality. In these poems, Ramalinga says, for instance, 'You may gain the boon of deathlessness' (4), 'we may gain the blessing of deathlessness' (21), 'why won't you not gain the great boon of not dying?' (25), 'my creed is the true creed that does away with death' (36). Some interpreters have concluded that Ramalinga's conquest of death refers to the state of the delivered soul in union with the Divine. Ramalinga was not an advaitist; in fact, he pours scorn on those who claim 'I am Brahman'. In Teyvamanimalai 2 he speaks of the delusive intelligence of the advaitists who claim that they are Brahman. It is (according to him) 'the type of intelligence which calls a rope a snake'; he calls their opinions 'foolish creed'. Ramalinga's philosophical basis seems to have been Saiva Siddhanta according to which the soul is coeval with the godhead, equally eternal, and not created by God. Now according to some interpreters of Ramalinga's poetry, when he speaks of immortality he means the state of union with the godhead after disembodiment; this union being eternal, there will be no more birth in human body, and hence no more death.[35] However, I am convinced that this interpretation is quite wrong. Ramalinga in fact quite clearly stresses the fact - more than once - that his body has become 'perfect gold'; that it is possible to prevent approaching death; that it is possible to live in

---

32 tantaiyai-k kanten nan caka varam perren.

33 maranamil lavaram nanperru-k konten.

34 maranamila-p-peru-valvu: the phrase itself is Ramalinga's; it appears in stanzas 1 and 23.

35 Thus, e.g., G. Vanmikanathan in *Pathway to God trod by Saint Ramalingar*, Bombay, 1976.

the great deathless life.[36] Nothing can be more obvious than when he says, 'my body has become golden-hued, and never-dying state has accrued to me'; and, 'my body of aged and wrinkled skin turned into a golden body'. Whether or not this is foolish delusion, thus indeed spoke the Siddhas. And as is evident from the poems translated below in full, Ramalinga speaks clearly the language of the Siddhas, and shares their fantastic and hardly credible belief that it is possible to conquer death in this life itself.

I begged my Father[37] to bestow on me a body,[38]
shining and for ever imperishable,
[indissolvable] either by wind, earth, fire or water,
by sun and other [heavenly bodies], by death or disease,
murderous weapons or planets, by violent actions
performed by others, or by other [factors];
he hastened to grant [it] to me.
O worldly people, do not think
lightly and with contempt of it!
Come and join the Lord of the Great Light of Grace! [39]

A powerful quatrain which calls the body Rambha (Tamil Arambai) who in Hindu mythology was the whore of the gods, says

This Arambai of maggots, made of patched up, diseased dross,
shines, transformed, in eternal, steady light by having joined the Pure
Good Path of siddhis' might, it's true, it's true, O people of this world!

Another poem - or rather part of a poem - says unmistakably,

Blemish is gone, and gone is want,
Foul flesh of vileness disappeared,
Wrinkles of old age gone away,
And grey hair faded out.
The dark veil's been completely shed.

---

36 *maranam illa peru valvu.*

37 *entai* (DEDR 3067) 'my father; our father, my elder brother; master, lord.'

38 Tamil original says clearly *mey* < Dravidian **mey* (DEDR 5073) 'body'.

39 *arut peruncoti iraivan.*

I will not sleep or die like people of the world.
I will not sleep, come to me, Lord.
I will not die, come to me, Lord. [40]
The four Vedas, the Agamas, and all sastras
are wisdom for the market,
not our own wisdom.
I have learned the science of deathlessness [41]
on the pure good path of the Absolute,
I have come towards the end of the Realm where the Lord
of Beyond nourishes everyone.
If you long for deathlessness, my friend,[42] you, too,
come play at bali, not saying this or that,
come play at ball, beholding Great Light of Grace.

Cf. especially the final verses of stanza 23 of the collection in question:

Note that we can live the Deathless great life!
I'm not indulging in fancy, I'm not telling lies.
I am telling the truth.
This is indeed the moment to enter
the Golden Hall, the Hall of Being.

And elsewhere (Tiruvuntiyar) he says openly, 'I have become a Siddha/bounce for joy! '

To the great noise raised by women,
to the surging noise of the drums,
accompanied by bizarre dance,
you wash the corpse,
and take it away
and burn it.
You corpses yet to die!
If at least the vultures would eat it

---

[40] Impossible in a translation to reproduce the phonaesthetic play of the original based on the similarity in sound between *uranka* [uranga] to sleep and *iranka* [iranga] to die (lit. 'to fall, descend ').

[41] Tamil *caka vittai.*

[42] In the original, *toli*, i.e. 'female companion, female friend'; in this context, the best translation would perhaps be 'sister'.

it would be of some use.
By burning it,
there's only ash
to be found.
It won't be suitable as manure
even for the dry lands.
(Camati varpuruttal)

Prose Texts

The two very short prose-portions introduced here as illustrations of late medieval Siddha non-poetic writings show quite well the difficulties involved in understanding and appreciating these texts. The first is a running prose-commentary on various stanzas which are either culled from earlier Siddha writings in verse, or which may have been composed ad hoc by the author of this commentary himself. He is named as Arunacala Kuru, and the work is called *Nijananta potam*, literally 'One's own delightful knowledge'. The text in question comments upon stanzas by Tirumular; according to one edition, it is the beginning of a gloss on Tirumantiram 2011, 2008 and 2010 (in this order). However, the standard edition of Tirumantiram (Kazhagam, Madras, 1975) numbers the respective stanzas as 1974, 1971 and 1973, and the commentary by Iramanata Pillai is very different from the Siddha prose text translated here. The Tirumantiram stanzas begin: 'Life-Essence, which desires [to incarnate] - [its] flowing downwards. . . ' etc. The Siddha prose-commentator says:

'If [a man] thinks with desire of a woman and unites in copulation [with her who] is pregnant with the embryo of the shape of up-to-one-day animalcules which had been like so many atoms in the man's sperm, and the animalcules of the semen mix with the woman's blood in the womb, there is no harm. . . The embryo will remain there. The two minds must stay in agreement. In the best copulation of that kind the mind of the woman must be fixed on the man's form. Her mind should not be fixed on any other form. If, while the two are in union, their minds are intensely fixed on the man, [it, i.e. the foetus] will have the shape of the man. If that longing intention is fixed on the sweetheart, the shape will be [that] of the respective mother.' Etc.

The second illustration is from the same text (Nijananta potam, pp. 530-31) and deals with various mantras (spells and magic formulae).

'The Siddhas' opinion is that, in employing mantras in order to get rid of diseases etc., one should not pronounce them aloud but contemplate them silently in one's mind. To overcome all disease and chase away demons, one should fix a Ganapati made of turmeric, place on it blossoms of the grass Cynodon dactylon, offer betel-leaf, coconut and plantains, and light an incense, fix one's inner stare onto the middle of the forehead, spread sacred ash in the palm of the left hand and write into it the pranava Om, repeat silently in contemplation 1008 times the mantra *am cin kili*, and then give the sacred ash to the sick person to swallow. To stop the pangs of childbirth, one should mix honey with breast-milk and give it to the pregnant woman to swallow while contemplating 16 times the mantra *om ciri cicu* (literally 'om laugh, baby'). At the time of delivery, one should smear on the belly of the woman butter and contemplate the mantra *tam tam*; the pains will cease and childbirth proceed easily. To burst venereal boils, ulcers etc. and diminish swellings, one should smear on the butter while repeating the mantra *um van tam on rin naci maci*, or swallow sacred ash while repeating the mantra *um van tam*.

To stop irritation in the eyes, purblindness, burning in the eyes, throbbing eye-pain and cataract, one should pour clean water into a container and wash the eyes contemplating intensively the mantra *la lu li*. As antidote to poisoning, one should drink water while repeating silently 108 times the mantra *om kili naci naci*.

To avert all kinds of trouble, one should repeat the mantra *om ran rin yanama civa cakala papa nivaraniyami*.

Versified medical texts

Kirikainul 64 ascribed to Akattiyar deals with some eighteen varieties of functional psychoses. Contemporary psychiatrists have identified some of the author's phenomenological descriptions of mental illness as description of schizophrenia and maniacal excitements.

With reasoning devoid
he will tear all his dresses,
smear faeces on his nakedness
and roll aimlessly in mud.
He'll eat his faeces,
knock his head on the floor,
drench himself in rain,
eat ashes and splash
water on his head.
(identified as chronic schizophrenia)

The following instances of versified description of mental diseases are gathered from Yoki cintamani 800 and Teraiyar vakatam.

He will remain sleepless,
dejected,
speech and food
rejected,
eyes bloody,
filled with anguish,
body pale and painful,
skin dry,
saliva drools in plenty,
he vomits,
he's giddy,
sad beyond words.
(identified as depressive psychosis)

Empty star
Eyes rolling
Speech slurred
Tongue dry
Throat filled with phlegm

Limbs stiff
Lost consciousness
Convulsions fast like gale
Sweating all over
Drenched in shit and urine
(identified as a kind of epilepsy)
Tirumular's *Tirumantiram* 492

Conclusion

Concluding this short reader of Siddha texts I wish to quote a handful of poems by Ramalinga Svami (1823-1874) which show that he at least was convinced to have gained genuine immortality. These verses were culled from numbers 4727, 4853, 6481 and 5295 of his great collection of poems.

1
I have sloughed of my troubles
I have forsaken worries
I've finished with perturbations
I've torn to pieces the Law of Birth and Death
I have abandoned sleep
I've left behind disease and death

2
O you great thief!
You sinner!
Death!
Run, Death, leave me alone!
And do not leave a trace behind,
crossing the earth and heavens,
crossing the vast dark spaces
which envelope them all.
If you won't leave,
if you will stay,
I will slay you
in a bloody way!
Run, Death,
leave me alone,
for I am well protected
by the Lord Who owns me.

3
Rid am I of misery!
I have abandoned all fears
which are now on the run.
I have vanquished all obstacles,
I am rid of the weariness of death.
And I have crossed the sea of rebirth.

4
Beat the drum, drummer, and say,
'I became effulgence of Grace.'
Beat the drum, drummer, and say,
'I gained the kingship o'er grace.'
Beat the drum, drummer, and say,
'I have got rid of delusion.'
Beat the drum, drummer, and say,
'I have done with death!'

Select Bibliography

Agehananda Bharati, *The Ochre Robe: An Autobiography.* 1st ed. 1962, Doubleday ed., 1970.

----, *The Tantric Tradition.* London, 1965.

----, *Great Tradition and Little Tradition: Indological Investigations in Cultural Anthropology.* Varanasi, 1978.

Arasu, S. R. V., *Voice of Vallalar.* Madras, 1974.

Arunachalam, M., *An Introduction to the History of Tamil Literature.* Tiruchitrambalam, 1974.

---------------, 'The Mysticism of Tirumular', *Ind. Philos. Annual* 11, 1976.

Balakrishnan, A., *English Renderings of Thiru Arutpa* (Selected Verses). Madras, 1966

Brosse, Thérèse, *Etudes expérimentales des techniques du Yoga, expérimentation psychosomatique.* Paris, 1963.

Buck, D., 'The Snake in the Song of a Sittar', *Structural Approaches to South Indian Studies*, 1971, 162 - 83.

Chitty, Simon Casie, *The Tamil Plutarch.* Colombo, 1946

Caravaṉamuttup Pillai, Va. (ed), *Periya ñâṉakkôvai*. Ceṉṉai, 1967.

Compte rendu du 1er Congrès International des Sciences Neurologiques de Bruxelles, 3, Pergamon Press, 1959.

Conditionnement et réactivité en électroencephalographie. Paris, Masson, 1957.

Dandapani Desikar, S., *Introduction to Tirumular's Tirumantiram.* Adheenam Publ. 97-A, Tiruvavaduturai, 1956.

Eliade, Mircea, *Yoga, Immortality and Freedom*. Princeton, 1969.

Filliozat, J., *Magie et médecine*. Paris, 1943.

-----, *La doctrine classique de la médecine indienne*. Paris, 1949.

Garrison, Omar, *Tantra the Yoga of Sex.* Avon Books, New York, 1964; repr. 1973.
Hittleman, Richard, *Yoga For Physical Fitness.* New Jersey, 1964.
Mookerjee, R. K., *Rasa-jala-niddh; or, Ocean of Indian Chemistry and Alchemy.* Calcutta, 1926 - 38.
Murugesa Mudaliar., C. S., *Materia medica* (Vegetable Section), ed. by Govindasamy Mudaliar, S, 3rd ed., Govt. of Tamil Nadu Publications. Madras, 1969.
Nau, Heinrich, *Prolegomena zu Pattanattu Pillaiyars Padal.* Halle, 1919.
Palarâmayyâ, Vi., *Muppû kuru.* Madras, 1971.
Patârtta ku<u>n</u>a pôti<u>n</u>i, ed. by Palarâmayyâ, Vi. Madras, 1975.
Râmanâta<u>n</u>, Aru. (ed.), *Cittar pâtalkal (Cittar periya ñâ<u>n</u>akkôvai e<u>n</u>a va<u>l</u>ankum . . .).* Madras, 3rd., 1968 (1st ed. 1959).
Ray, Prafulla Chandra, *A History of Hindu Chemistry*, 2nd ed. Calcutta, 1904 -09.
Shanmuga Velan, A., *Siddhars' Science of Longevity and Kalpa Medicine of India.* Madras, Sakthi Nilayam, 1963.
Singaravelu Mudaliar, A., *Abithana Chintamani. The Enclyclopedia of Tamil Literature* (in Tamil). Repr. New Delhi, 1981.
Stearn, J., *Yoga, Youth and Reincarnation.* New York, 1968.
Steever, S., 'The theological underpinnings of Civavâkkiyam'. Paper presented at the 12th Annual Meeting of the Mid-Atlantic Region of the *Association of Asian Studies.* Univ. of Pennsylvania, Oct. 30, 1983.
Steever, Sanford B., *Civavâkkiyar's Abecedarium Naturae* (manuscript copy). s.d.
Stevens, John, *Lust for Enlightenment, Buddhism and Sex.* Shambhala, Boston and London, 1990.
Subramania Aiyar, A. W., *The Poetry and the Philosophy of the Tamil Siddhas: An Essay in Criticism.* Tirunelveli, 1957. Chidambaram, 1969.
Theos, Bernard, *Hatha-Yoga: The Report of a Personal Experience.* New York, 1944.
Tirumûla Nâya<u>n</u>âr . . . *Tirumantiram.* With comm. by Pa. Irâmanâta Pi<u>l</u>lai, notes by A. Citampara<u>n</u>âr. Kazhagam, Madras, 1974. 2 vols.
Uthamaroyan, C. S., *Siddha Hospital Pharmacopoea.* Govt. of Tamil Nadu Publications, Madras, 1967.
Vanmikanathan, G., *Pathway to God trod by Saint Ramalingar.* Bombay, Bharatiya Vidya Bhavan, 1976.
Va<u>t</u>ivêlu Mutaliyâr, Mâ. (ed.) *Civavâkkiyar pâ<u>t</u>al.* With comm. Madras, 1970.

Vênukôpâlap Pillai, Mê. Vî., Vittuvân̲ (ed.), *Cittar ñân̲ak kôvai*. 2nd ed., Madras, 1956.
Vishnudevananda, Swami, *The Complete Illustrated Book of Yoga*. New York, 1972.
Wiener Zeitschrift für Nervenheilkunde und deren Grenzgebiete. Wien, 1958.
Zvelebil, Kamil, *The Smile of Murugan: On Tamil Literature of South India*. Leiden, E. J. Brill, 1974 (chapter 14).
------, V., *The Poets of the Powers*. London, Rider, 1973, repr., Integral Publishing, Lower Lake, California, 1993.
-----, *I maestri dei poteri. I Siddha tamil dell'India*. Ubaldini Editore, Roma, 1979 (Ital. version of 1973).
-----, *Tamil Literature*. Wiesbaden, Otto Harrassowitz, 1974.
-----, 'The Philosophy of Tamil Siddhas', lecture, *Hebrew University*, Jerusalem, 6.6.1985.
Also, a specific study, Daniel E. Valentine, 'The Pulse as an Icon in Siddha Medicine', *Contributions to Asian Studies*, Leiden, 18, 1984, 115-26

Index

This index contains Tamil and Sanskrit terms used in this book. As given here, they represent correct transliterations with diacritical markings. Only such terms are included which require diacritics in the transliterated forms, e.g., Tamil iruḷ (irul in the text), 'darkness' is included whereas, e.g., Sanskrit deha (deha in the text) is not. Also, the simplest possible translation / interpretation is given with the entries.

aṉupāṉam - anupanam, supporting drug

apalanāṭi - apalanati, weak pulse

apāṉaṉ - apanan, vital air going downwards

apatya patārtta - apatya patartta, incompatible substance in diet

aṟam - aram, dharma, cosmic and moral order

araṉ - aran, Hara, a name of Vishnu

āṟātāram - arataram, six nerve plexuses, six chakras

aritāram - aritaram, yellow sulphuret of arsenic

aruḷ - arul, grace

aṟuvai - aruvai, surgery

āsana - asana, position, posture, yogic or meditaive posture

āśrama - asrama, order, stage of life

aṣṭa mā citti - asta ma citti, eight great powers

aṣṭamūlam - astamulam, eightfold root

aṣṭāṅga yoga -astanga yoga, eightfold yoga

aśuddha - asuddha, impure

aśvinī mudrā - asvini mudra, method of holding breath with anal contraction

āṭkāṭṭi - atkatti, forefinger

ātman - atman, immanent absolute spirit

āttuma tattuvam - attuma tattuvam, faculty of soul

Auvaiyār - Auvaiyar, ancient Tamil poetess

avidyā - avidya, ignorance

avyakṛtavastūni - avyakrtavastuni, matters which cannot be answered by logical predication, imponderables

Ayaṉ - Ayan, the Lord, name of god Brahma

Āyurveda - Ayurveda, ancient Indian medical system

baindavaśarīra - baindavasarira, body composed of bindu

bālā - bala, girl, maid

Bālā - Bala, a goddess

bhū - bhu, earth

Brahmā - Brahma, one of the gods of the Hindu trinity, the creator

Bṛhadāranyakopaniṣad - Brhadaranyakopanisad, ancient Indian philosophical text

cākā vittai - caka vittai, science of deathlessness

cakrapūjā - cakrapuja, tantrik ritual

camāṉaṉ - camanan, equality

caṉṉi - canni, apoplexy

caṉṉināṭi - canninati, apoplectic pulse

carumappuṇ - carumappun, dermatitis

Caṭṭaimuṇi - Cattaimuni, medieval Siddha author

cāvu - cavu, death

cavvīram - cavviram, medicinal compound of several minerals

cempañcu kuḷampu - cempancu kulampu, kind of cosmetic cream

Ceyyōṉ - Ceyyon, The Red One, one of the names of Murugan

ciciṉam - cicinam, phallus

Cikāmaṇiveṇpā - Cikamanivenpa, work by Tēraiyar on medicine

Cilappatikāram - Cilappatikaram, The Lay of the Anklet; ancient Tamil narrative poem (ca. 450-550 AD)

cilēṭṭumam - cilettumam, phlegm

cintūram - cinturam, red colour; red chemical preparation from metals or minerals

cirōṇitam - cironitam, menstrual blood

ciṟunīr - cirunir, urine

ciṟupañcamūlam - cirupancamulam, little fivefold root

cittamātrā - cittamatra, lit. mind only; school of Mahāyāna Buddhism

cittaṉ - cittan, Siddha

cittāntam - Siddhanta, philosophical system and school

Cittarārūṭaccintu - Cittararutaccintu, Siddha work on toxicology

Cittarārūṭam - Cittararutam, Siddha work on toxicology

Cittar ñāṉakkōvai - Cittar nanakkovai, volume of Siddha poetry

Cīvakacintāmaṇi - Civakacintamani, Tamil epic poem of tenth century

civakuṭinīr muppū - civakutinir muppu, muppu, the liquid drunk by Siva

civampū - civampu, elixir of life

Civañāṉavaḷḷai - Civananavallai, medieval Tamil Saiva poet

Civavākkiyam - Civavakkiyam, aphorism on Siva by Civavākkiyar

Civavākkiyar - Civavakkiyar, medieval Tamil Siddha poet

Civavīriyam - Civaviriyam, mercury

civāyanama - civayanama, sacred mantra Hail to Siva

cōmavātam - comavatam, elixir of life

cōṇitam - conitam, menstrual blood

cōti - coti, lustre, light

cōtippul - cotippul, a kind of grass

cukkāṉ - cukkan, kunkur limestone

cūkkuma pūtaṅkaḷ - cukkuma putankal, subtle elements

cūkṣma carīram - cuksma cariram, subtle body

cūṉiyam - cuniyam, void, emptiness

curatanīr - curatanir, female secretion before and during coitus

Cūriyāṉantar Ñāṉacūttiram - Curiyanantar Nanacuttiram, a Siddha treatise curōṇitam - curonitam, menstrual blood

cuṭar - cutar, lustre, light

Dakṣa - Daksa, name of a demon

Devī - Devi, the goddess

dhāraṇā - dharana, concentration

dhyāna - dhyana, meditation

ēlam - Elettaria cardamomum, cardamom

e<u>l</u>uvakai tātu - eluvakai tatu, seven constituents of the body

eṇvikāram - en vikaram, eight passions

guṇa - guna, quality

Hakīm Mukammatu Aptullā - Hakim Mukammatu Aptulla, author on Siddha medicine

Haṭha Yoga - Hatha Yoga, basic kind of yoga, yoga of the body

hīṅg - hing, asafoetida

iḷanīr - ilanir, juice of fresh coconut

iñcivēr - ginger plant, fresh ginger

iracavātam - iracavatam, alchemy

iracavāti - iracavati, alchemist

iracāya<u>n</u>am - iracayanam, elixir of life

iṟaiva<u>n</u> - iraivan, lord, king, god

Irāmatēvar - Iramatevar, legendary Siddha

Irāmatēvar Civayōkam - Iramatevar Civayokam, Siddha work on medicine and worship

iraṭṭaināṭi - irattainati, coupled pulse; corpulent person

iruḷ - irul, darkness

iśitva - isitva, supremacy

īśvarī - Isvari, the Goddess

iṭaiviṭunāti - itaivitunati, intermittent pulse

Iṭaikkāṭṭuccittar - Itaikattu Cittar, medieval Siddha poet

Iṭaiyar - Itaiyar, cowherd caste

jātikkāy poṭi - jatikkay poti, powdered nutmeg

jīvanmukta - jivanmukta, person liberated in this life

Kaivalya navanītam - Kaivalya navanitam, Saivite philosophical work

kākkai vali - kakkai vali, epilepsy

kaḷ - kal, fermented sap, toddy

kalacapūṇṭu - kalacapuntu, bug-weed, pot-herb, moxa-weed

kālaiyil iñci kaṭumpakalcukku, in the morning fresh ginger, sharp at noon dry ginger

kāḷā<u>n</u> - kalan, mushroom Agaricus campestris

Kālī - Kali, wrathful aspect of the Goddess

kaḷimpu - kalimpu, verdigris or rust

kalpacāta<u>n</u>ai - kalpacatanai, quest of immortality

kāmanīr - kamanir, lit., 'lust juice', female discharge during coitus(?)

kāmappāl - kamappal, lit., 'milk of lust', female discharge during coitus(?)

kāmaśāstra - kamasastra, treatise on sex and love

kāmāvaśāyitva - kamavasayitva, fulfilment of desires

kampināṭi - kampinati, wiry pulse

kāmpu - kampu, nipple

ka<u>n</u><u>n</u>iyi<u>n</u> yō<u>n</u>i - virgin's vagina

kantakaracaya<u>n</u>am - kantakarasayanam, life-prolonging medicine

karaṇacarīram - karanacariram, supersubtle body

karaṇai - karanai, medicinal plant

karaṇavuṭal - karanavutal, supersubtle body

karicālai - karicalai, Eclipta alba

kaṟiyuppu - kariyuppu, kitchen salt

kaṟṟāḻai - karralai, Indian aloes

kāṟṟu - karru, wind

kārttikai - kartikai, month of November-December

karumēntiriyam - karumentiriyam, five organs of motor action

kaṭal nurai - katal nurai, sea-foam, Meerschaum

kati nāṭi - katinati, hard pulse

kaṭukkāy - katukkay, Terminalia chebula

Kaṭuveḷiccittar - Katuveli Cittar, medieval Siddha poet

kauri cintāmaṇi centūram - kauri cintamani centuram, a kind of drug

Kāvēri-p-paṭṭiṉam - Kaveri-p-pattinam, harbour and capital of Chola kingdom

kāyacitti - kayacitti, Siddha science of longevity; life prolonging medicine

kāyacittaccuṇam - kayacittaccunam, kind of gypsum used as longevity drug

kāyacittiyāṉōṉ - kayacittiyanon, person who attained power of kayacitti

kāyacittiyuppu - kayacittiyuppu, urine salt

kāyakalpa - kayakalpa, longevity drug

kāyam - kayam, body

kāyakaṟpam - kayakarpam, longevity drug

khecarīmudrā - khecarimudra, arresting expiration by tongue

kīḻānelli - kilanelli, Phyllanthus Niruri

kiḻaṅku - kilanku, tuber, root

kīlvāyu - kilvayu, arthritic or rheumatic joint disorders

kīṟal - kiral, incision

kōḻi - koli, fowl

Koṅkaṇa Nātar - Konkana Natar, medieval Siddha poet

Koṅkaṇar - Konkanar, Siddha teacher and poet

kōrai - korai, Cyperus rotundus

kōraikkiḻaṅku - koraikkilanku, root of Cyperus rotundus

koṟukkuppuṇ - korukkuppun, chancroid

kukkippuṇ - kukkippun, lit., 'belly wound', stomach ulcer

kuḻi - kuli, lit., 'hole', vagina

kumiḻ - kumil, lit., 'knob', clitoris

kuṇḍalinī - kundalini, vital force residing in human body

kuṉmam - kunman, stomach disease

Kuṟavar - Kuravar, nomadic community of South India

Kūrmāṉantar Ñānacūttiram 5O - Kurmanantar Nanacuttiram 5O, a Siddha treatise

kūrnāṭi - kurnati, sharp pulse

Kurunāṭiccūttiram - Kurunaticcuttiram, medical treatise ascribed to Akattiyar

kuruti vāṅkal - kuruti vankal, blood letting

Kuṭampaiccittar - Kutampai Cittar, medieval Siddha poet

kutiraivōṭṭam - kutiraivottam, horse-gallop

Liṅgapurāṇa - Lingapuranam, Saivite purāṇa in Sanskrit

Māhāyana - Mahayana, lit., 'great vehicle', Buddhism as practiced in Central and East Asia

māmicam - mamicam, meat

maittuṉam - maittunam, coitus

Maṇiveṇpā - Manivenpa, treatise ascribed to Tēraiyar

maṇṭalam - mantalam, region

mantravādin - mantravadin, person who knows and uses spells

Maṟaiñāṉacampantar - Marainanacampantar, medieval Saivite Tamil scholar

maraṇam illāmai - maranam illamai, immortality

maraṇamilī-p-peru vāḻvu - maranamili-p-peru valvu, great deathless life

maraṇanāṭi - marananati, deathless pulse

mārga - marga, way, path

marukkoḻuntu - marukkoluntu, Artemisia vulgaris

muruḷ - marul, delusion

Maruttuppāratam - Maruttupparatam, medical work ascribed to Tēraiyar

māttirai - mattirai, measure

māyā - maya, illusion, matter

māyai - mayai, illusion, matter

mēkkappuṇ - mekappun, syphilis; chancre

mēkaveṭṭai - mekavettai, gonorrhoea

meṉāṭi - menati, feeble pulse

Meyññāṉappulampal - Meynnanappulampal, poems by Pattirakiriyar

mōr - mor, curdled milk; buttermilk; yoghurt

mōtiraviral - motiraviral, ring-finger

muccukkalāyam - muccukkalayam, moxa treatment

mudrā - mudra, gesture

mukkuṇam - mukkunam, three qualities

mūlabandha - mulabandha, anal contraction (yoga)

mūladhāra - root-centre in body (yoga)

mulaippāl - mulaippal, mother's (breast) milk

Mūlaṉ - Mulan, a cowherd, Tirumūlar

mūlatāram - root-centre in body (yoga)

mūṉṟu, adj. mu-/mū- - munru, mu-, three

mūṉṟu maṇṭalam - munru mantalam, three regions of the body

muppiṇi - muppini, three humours

muppū - muppu, substance used in Siddha quest for longevity

murdāsiṅgh -murdasingh, Plumbi oxidum

Murukaṉ - Murukan, probably indigenous South Indian god

mūttiram - muttiram, urine

nātam - natam, destruction

Nacciṉārkkiṉiyar - Naccinarkkiniyar, medieval Tamil commentator (14th c.)

Nākamuṉi nayaṉaviti - Nakamuni nayanaviti, work on ophthalmology and surgery

Ñāṉacātirattiraṭṭu - Nanacatirattirattu, Siddha text

ñāṉam - nanam, knowledge

ñāṉapintu - nanapintu, see muppū

Nandīśa - Nandisa, Siva's theriomorphic form of white bull

ñāṉēntiriyam - nanentiriyam, five organs of perception

Nārāyaṇa Kōṉār - Narayana Konar

nāśa - nasa, destruction

nātacayam - natacayam, ovary

nātakkuḻal - natakkulal, Fallopian tubes

nātakkumiḻ - natakkumil, Graafian vesicles

nātam - natam, sound

nātam - natam, semen muliebre, female sex-discharge

nātam pintam - natam pintam, see muppū

nātaṉ - natan, sir, lord, Lord

Naṭarāja - Nataraja, Siva as the Lord of Dance

patya patārtta - patya patartta, compatible substances in diet

pāvi - pavi, sinner

peṇcarakku - pencarakku, female substances

Perumpāṇāṟṟuppaṭai - Perumpanarruppatai, ancient Tamil poem (c. 200 AD)

peruṅkāya cūraṇam - perunkaya curanam, Siddha remedy against indigestion

perupañcamūlam - perupancamulam, large fivefold root

pētiyuṟai - petiyurai, laxative

pīccal - piccal, enema

piṇṭamuppū - pintamuppu, embryo-muppū

pirāṇaṉ - piranan, vital air

pittanīr - pittanir, bile

pōki - poki, one who enjoys; happy person

pōṟṟi - porri, praise; applause; hail

praṇava - pranava, designation of the mystic syllable oṃ

prākāmya - prakamya, irrestible will

prāṇa - prana, respiratory breath; cosmic breath; vital air; vital force

prāṇāyama - pranayama, controlled breathing, breathing exercise

Prasannapāda - Prasannapada, Buddhist text

pratyahāra - pratyahara, emancipation of sensory activities

pūjā - puja, worship, ritual

pū - pu, flower, blossom

puṇarcci - joining; coitus

pūnīr muppū - punir muppu, earth-water muppū

pūppu - puppu, flowering, blossoming; menstruation, esp., first menses

pūtanāṭi - putanati, a kind of pulse

pūttamaṅkai - puttamankai, lit., woman [who] has flowered, [freshly] menstruating woman

rasavāda - rasavada, alchemy

Rasavāta (Iracavāta) cintāmaṇi - Rasavata cintamani, treatise on alchemy and chemical processes

racavātam - racavatam, alchemy

racavāti - racavati, alchemist

rasāyana - rasayana, elixir of life

Rāmaliṅka Cuvāmi - Ramalinga Svami (1823-1974). Tamil poet

rōki - roki, sick person

sādhanā - sadhana, performance, worship, ritual, accomplishment, fulfilment, perfection

Śaiva siddhānta - Śaiva Siddhanta, medieval South Indian philosophical system

śakti - sakti, Sakti, lit., force, potence; cosmic force; its personification as consort of gods

samādhi - samadhi, here, enstasis; also concentration; trance

saṃdhābhāṣā - sandhabhasa, twilight language, metaphoric speech, ellusive speech; professional jargon of the Siddhas

saṃdhyābhāṣā - sandhyabhasa, see saṃdhābhāṣā

saṃyama - samyama, lit., holding together; control, self-control; concentration of mind; meditation

Śatapathabrāhmaṇa - Ṣatapathabrahmana, ancient Sanskrit text, part of Vedic literature

Śiva - Siva, god of Hindu Trinity, the Destroyer; but also the Benevolent

śivabījā -sivabija, mercury

śivamśakti, see muppū

śivāyanama - sivayanama, 'hail to Siva', sacred mantra

śleṣman - slesman, phlegm

Śrī Vaiṣṇavī - Sri Vaisnavi, a goddess

śruti - sruti, lit., hearing; that which is heard, revealed; revelation

stūla pūtam - stula putam, gross element

stūla sarīram - stula sariram, gross body

śuddha - suddha, pure, clean

śukla - sukla, whiteness; sperm

śukra tyāg kare - sukra tyag kare (Hindi), abandoning the semen

śūnya - sunya, emptiness, void; empty

tacamūlam - tacamulam, tenfold root

taca nāṭi - taca nati, ten nerves

taca vāyu - taca vayu, ten vital airs

Takkaṉ - Takkan, Daksa, name of a demon

taḷampunāti - talampunati, undulating pulse

tāmpira centūram - tampira centuram. Siddha drug against peptic ulcer

tāṉṟi - tanri, Terminalis belerica

Tāṇṭavarāya Cuvāmikaḷ - Tantavaraya Cuvamikal (17th c.) Saiva philosopher

Tāṇṭavarāya Kōṉār - Tantavaraya Konar

Taṉvantiri nikaṇṭu - Tanvantiri nikantu, a medieval lexicon

Taṉvantiri vaittiyam - Tanvantiri vaittiyam, Siddha medical treatise

tavaḷai - tavalai, frog

taṭaṅkunāṭi - tatakunati, halting pulse

Tattuvarāyar - Tattuvarayar, great medieval Tamil poet

tātu - tatu, humour (medic.)

tayircunti cūraṇam - tayircunti curanam, drug from dry ginger and

tayircunti cūraṇam - tayircunti curanam, drug from dry ginger and fermented curds with mineral salts

Tāyumāṉavar - Tayumanavar (17th c.), great Tamil mystic and poet

tēkam - tekam, body

Teṉṉāṭu - Tennatu, Southern India

tērai - terai, toad

Tēraiyar - Teraiyar, student of Agastya, a Siddha

Tēraiyar (yamaka) veṇpā - Teraiyar (yamaka) venpa, medical treatise

Tēvar - Tevar, other name of Konkana Nayanar

tēyu - teyu, fire

Teyvamaṇimālai - Teyvamanimalai, poem by Ramalinga Svami

tirikaṭucūraṇam - tirikatucuranam, three-pungents powder

tirikaṭukam - tirikatukam, threefold pungency

Tirikaṭukam - Tirikatukam, collection of didactic maxims, c. 725 AD

tirikaṭuku - tirikatuku, three stimulants

tiri nāṭi - tiri nati, three nerve-channels

tiripalacūraṇam - tiripalacuranam, powder of three sorts of myrobalam

Tīrthaṅkara - Tirthankara, Jaina saint (arhat)

Tiruvēkampamālai - Tiruvekampamalai, collection of poems by Pattinattar

Tirukkuṟaḷ - Tirukkural, (c. 450 AD), well-known Tamil collection of didactic philosophical couplets

Tirumūlar - Tirumular, early medieval Tamil poet, author of Tirumantiram

Tirumuṟai - Tirumurai, 5iva canonical literature

tirunīṟu - tiruniru, sacred ash

Tiruvaḷḷuva Nāyaṉār - Tiruvalluva Nayanar, Siddha author

Tiruvāvaṭutuṟai - Tiruvavatuturai, a sacred place and large monastery in Tamilnatu

Tiruvēṅkaṭa Ceṭṭiyār - Tiruvenkata Cettiyar, proper name of Pattinattar

Tiruviṭaimarutūr mummaṇikkōvai - Tiruvitaimarutur mummanikkovai, devotional poem by Paṭṭiṉattaṭikaḷ

Tiruvoṟṟiyūr - Tiruvorriyur, holy place near Madras

Tiruvuntiyār - Tiruvuntiyar, poem by Ramalinga Svami

tīviranāṭi - tiviranati, fast pulse

tivyataṉu - tivyatanu, divine body

tokkaṇam, tokkaṭam - tokkanam, tokkatam, physiotherapeutic massage

tōḻi - toli, female friend

Tolkāppiyam Poruḷatikāram - Tolkappiyam Porulatikaram, third part of the most ancient Tamil grammar

toyyil kuḻampu - toyyil kulampu, kind of cosmetic cream

tulsī - tulsi, sacred basil (Ocymum sanctum)

tuḷḷunāṭi - tullunati, irregular pulse

tuṇai maruntu - tunai maruntu, supporting drug; conjoint therapy

tuṇṇāṭi - tunnati, small pulse

tuṭināṭi - tutinati, abrupt pulse

uḷanōy - ulanoy, mental disease

ullāsa - ullasa, chapter, section of a book

Umā - Uma, goddess, consort of Siva

Umāpati Civācārya - Umapati Civavarya (13th-14th c.), Saiva philosopher uṇavu maruntu maruntē uṇavu, (Tamil saying) food is drug and drug is food

Upaniṣads - Upanisads, ancient Indian philosophical texts

upāya - upaya, statagem, craft, artifice, skillfull means

Urōmariṣi ñāṉam - Uromarisi nanam, medieval Siddha medical treatise

uṟpatti - urpatti, origin

ūtal - utal, blowing

uṭal nōy - utal noy, physical disease

utaranāṭi - utaranati, abdominal pulse

uvar maṇṇuppu - uvar mannuppu, salt of saline soil

uyarveḷi - uyarveli, highest light (or highest emptiness or void)

Vaikāci - Vaikaci, month of May-June

vaittiyaṉ - vaittiyan, Siddha physician

Vaittiya navanītam - Siddha medical treatise

Vajrayāṇa - Vajrayana, Tantrik school in Buddhism

Vālai - Valai, a goddess

vālaikkummi - valaikkummi, female dance in honour of Valai

vallārai - vallarai, Hydrocotyle asiatica

Vaḷḷi- - Valli, consort of god Murugan

vamaṇa maruntu - vamana maruntu, emetic

vaṇṇāṭi - vannati, strong pulse

vaṉṉi - vanni, fire salt

varṇa - varna, basic unit of Hindu social hierarchy; there are four varṇas

varṇāśrama dharma - varnasrama dharma, Hindu doctrine of social classes and orders

vaśitva - vasitva, dominion over elements

vātam - vatam, utterance

vātam - vatam, air

vātamaiyuppu - vatamaiyuppu, (common) salt

vāyu - vayu, wind

vēl, karuvēl - vel, karuvel, Acacia arabica

Vēlaṉ - Velan, lit., Spear-bearer, one of the names of god Murugan

veḷiyiṟveḷi - veliyirveli, total emptiness, void in emptiness

veḷḷaikkal - vellaikkal, moon salt

veḷḷi - velli, whiteness; silver; sperm

vēmpu - vempu, margosa

veṇmai - venmai, whiteness

veṇpā - venpa, one of four main types of metres and stanzas

Vēṇukōpāla Piḷḷai, Mē. Vī. - Venukopala Pillai, M., V., Tamil scholar and editor

vēr - ver, root

veṟikkunāṭi - verikkunati, jerky pulse

veṟṟilainīr - verrilainir, betel juice

veṟṟilaippākku - verrilaippakku, areca-nut in betel leaf

veṭṭaveḷi - vettaveli, broad daylight or sheer emptiness

vibhūti - vibhuti, sacred ash

Vijñānavāda - Vijnanavada, philosophical school of Mahāyāna Buddhism

vikaṟpanāṭi - vikarpanati, unequal pulse

Vināyaka - Vinayaka, one of the names of the god Ganesha as remover of obstacles

vintunātam - male and female semen

Vi., Palarāmayyā - V. Balaramiah, contemporary author on Siddhism vīriyakkaṭṭu - viriyakkattu, thick consistency of sperm

vīriyam - viriyam, lit., vigour; sperm

Viṣṇu - Vishnu, god of the Hindu trinity, the Preserver

Yākkoppu, Yākūb, Yākob - Yakkopu, early legendary Siddha

Yogadarśana - Yogadarsana, a Sanskrit work on yoga

yōki - yoki, yogin

yōṉi - yoni, female sex-organ, vulva, vagina

yōṉiliṅkam - yonilinkam, clitoris

yōṉimaṇi - lit., jewel of yoni, clitoris

yōṉituvāram - yonituvaram, vagina

yōṉivāy - yonivay, mouth of yoni, vagina

Yūkimuṉi cāstiram - Yukimuni castiram, Siddha medical treatise

List of Illustrations